COPING WITH STRESS

HAMLYN HELP YOURSELF GUIDE

COPING WITH STRESS

HELEN DORE

HAMLYN

For Geoffrey, Mary and Richard

The Sample Stress Audit which appears on page 23 is
reproduced from *Action on Stress at Work*,
by Maggie Gee and Liz Reason, HEA, 1988,
by kind permission of the Health Education Authority.

First published in 1990
Hamlyn is an imprint of Octopus Illustrated Publishing
Michelin House, 81 Fulham Road,
London SW3 6RB
part of Reed International Books

Reprinted 1991

ISBN 0 600 56904 7

Typeset by Servis Filmsetting Manchester
Printed and bound in Great Britain
by Collins, Glasgow

CONTENTS

What is Stress?   6

Stress at Work   16

Stress at Home   33

Holiday and Travel Stress   47

Baby Stress   56

Children Under Stress   64

Stress in Old Age   74

State of Body
Stress Remedies   82

State of Mind
Stress Remedies   105

Sources of Help   112

ONE

WHAT IS STRESS?

Stress is an experience all of us share to a greater or lesser degree. The term 'stress' is very widely encountered in everyday use, and a great deal has been written about it in recent years at a variety of levels, from specialist studies by members of the medical profession, to features in popular weekly magazines.

The stress we usually hear and read about, and indeed experience ourselves as a widespread phenomenon of modern life, is most often the harmful, negative variety. We tend to associate it with disagreeable situations like getting held up in a traffic jam, overworking, or losing a job, and with unpleasant physical manifestations such as headache or even a heart attack.

The good news is that stress has a positive side too. In fact stress is all about energy, and as such can perhaps best be described as a dynamic, stimulating and motivating life-force. Life without it would be unbearably dull and featureless – indeed, in a totally stress-free existence nothing would ever be achieved! Any activity requiring effort creates stress, which can be seen, therefore, as a vital spur and incentive. It is stress in one form or another that literally gets us going – out of bed in the morning; across the road in an alert fashion. Stress motivates us to earn our living and enables us to concentrate in order to do a job efficiently and give our best performance. Another positive aspect of stress is that we can use it as a measure against which to test our reactions to a variety of situations and find out more about ourselves.

Understanding more about stress and how to handle it helps us to learn to make positive decisions and choices, and lead fuller, more rewarding lives as a result. So it is possible not only to come to terms with harmful stress, by developing a set of stress-skills that are right for you as an individual, but also to harness and channel stress generally to your advantage – an exciting prospect.

Obviously, how you choose to approach the stress-handling process is to some extent a very personal matter, but stress patterns and ways to deal with them occur and recur in quite similar areas in all our lives. By concentrating on these, this book sets out to discover how and why stress manifests itself in a variety of shared experiences and situations, and offers as many suggestions as possible for ways in which it can be tackled.

How stress works

This is a subtle process involving the interaction of mind and body, best understood if one thinks of stress as an adaptive mechanism involving alarms and responses, demand and compensation. First of all, a situation or set of circumstances, described as a 'stressor', sets off alarms in the mind, requiring a response. As we will see shortly, change in a variety of forms is one of the major stressors, manifesting itself in situations that are readily identifiable as stressful, such as bereavement, divorce, ill health, job loss. Other common causes of stress are decisions to be made; challenges to be met; environmental factors, especially noise and overcrowding, as in high-density urban living; attempting to take on too much; or, conversely, a monotonous existence resulting in loss of sense of direction or purpose. Even the daily news, all too often conveying disasters and atrocities, is a cause of stress.

Response to stressors is expressed both physically and psychologically, by the body and the mind. Healthy body reactions to stress are controlled by the autonomic (which means 'self-governing') nervous system. The so-called 'sympathetic' part of this system gears the individual for action, aided by the release of certain secreted hormones, in particular adrenalin, which work by circulating in the blood to stimulate the body's organs. Adrenalin equips the body for emergency action, constricting the arteries and accelerating the heart-beat rate, in order to rush an increased supply of blood to the muscles and brain. The adrenalin hormone also speeds up the metabolism by sending an increased supply of oxygen to the blood and stimulating the liver to release energy reserves in the form of glucose sugar, which enhances the performance of the muscles, brain and heart.

The action for which the system is now equipped may take the form of an engagement, or confrontation, or a withdrawal – this is why this stage in the stress process is often described as the 'fight or flight' principle. The temporary loss of balance caused by the 'sympathetic' side of the autonomic nervous system is then normally compensated by its 'parasympathetic' counterpart, which is responsible for ensuring rest, sleep, and an effective digestive system, so that the body remains in good working order.

When the sympathetic stimulative activity goes on for too long, uncompensated by the parasympathetic, then the potentially valuable energy that has been released goes into overdrive, creating excess, unrelieved, harmful stress. This is when pressures seem unmanageable and overwhelming, one of the most familiar mental symptoms of harmful stress. Or to put it another way, when the two complementary sides of the autonomic nervous system lose their natural balance in relation to each other, stress can no longer be described as healthy.

The chart on page 9 outlines the response pattern of stress. Column 1 summarizes the major initial changes in the body and the emotions resulting from the inaugural alarm signals emitted by the brain. Column 2 describes the immediate effects of these changes, all of which at this stage can be put to good use, provided the energy generated is released properly. If it is not, then adverse effects take over, as outlined in Column 3. If these are prolonged, or continue to recur over-frequently, then potentially serious stress-induced symptoms, both physical and mental, occur, as described in Column 4.

Stress and change

Stress means many different things to different people – it can even mean different things at different times to the same person – but one of its underlying characteristics is the frequency with which it is encountered in association with change. Harmful stress is often regarded as a disease endemic to the 20th century, and it cannot be a coincidence that a period that has witnessed such major changes in life at all levels, from the invention of the motor car to the appearance of the test tube baby, has also seen a most dramatic rise in stress levels. Coping successfully with stress is often a

1 Responses to Alarm Signals	2 Coping Abilities are Alerted	3 Adverse Effects of Unreleased Energy	4 Harmful Stress-induced Conditions
The adrenalin hormone is released into the bloodstream	Physical and mental faculties are put on full alert	Frustration; worry	Impatience with self and others; anxiety; insomnia
The liver is stimulated to release energy stored in the body as fat and sugar	Provision of instant energy	Inability to relax; hyperactivity	Irritability; fatigue; build-up of cholesterol in blood
Raised breathing rate	Increase of oxygen supply in bloodstream	Breathlessness	Dizziness; fainting fits
Raised pulse rate	Diffusion of oxygen	Raised blood pressure	Palpitations; headaches; hypertension; heart disease
Muscular tension	Readiness for action	Muscles remain tense, resulting in exhaustion	Aching in parts of body; trembling limbs; tics
Full arousal of mental faculties	Focusing of mental faculties	Irrational decisions; impulsive behaviour	Loss of concentration; impaired memory
Digestive process inhibited	Energy diverted to areas of body as required	Loss of appetite; 'butterflies' in stomach; nausea	Indigestion; constipation; ulcers
Increase in perspiration	Cooling down of body as it prepares for action	Clammy hands; profuse sweating	Nervous rashes; eczema
Need to empty bladder, evacuate bowels	Reduction of body weight as it gets ready for action	Very frequent urination; defecation	Stress incontinence
Emotional tension	Preparation for effort	Crying and nervous laughter; abrupt mood changes; aggression	Uncontrolled angry outbursts; depression

question of adapting adequately to change, and to meeting the many demands which change imposes, but the literally breath-taking speed and diversity of change within our own time has created an overwhelming range of choices, which can be confusing and stressful in their own right.

Yet natural, as opposed to artificially accelerated, change is the very essence of life itself. The great life-experiences which human beings share – for example, birth, marriage (and divorce), bereavement and so on – all involve a very considerable element of change.

It is when the response to these changes is in some way inadequate that they become stressful: then they are no longer natural transitions, but stumbling blocks. And the same is true of reactions to the major body changes – puberty, menstruation, pregnancy, the menopause – which are in themselves an entirely natural part of the life process, but potentially stressful in an adverse sense, depending on individual response.

On a more mundane level, many of the potentially stressful situations we encounter in our everyday lives are also linked to change – like moving away from home for the first time; starting a new job; moving house; taking retirement. While some of the ordinary ups-and-downs which we all encounter on an everyday basis may seem almost too insignificant in themselves to rank as stressful, they can easily become so if they accumulate over a long period of time.

Many of the stressful situations and suggestions for coping with them to be found in this book will be seen to be closely related to change, and one cannot emphasize too strongly that an awareness of the stress/change relation is one of the basic premises for learning to come to terms with stress. Obviously, change that is not of your own choosing, but seemingly imposed on you, will tend to be much more stressful than change which you can more easily control for yourself. But generally speaking, if you can get into the habit of anticipating change, thinking and planning ahead, and learning to balance changes in your life with a variety of compensating and stabilizing factors, you are off to a great start on the road to controlling stress rather than letting it take control of you.

Personality and stress levels

Contrary to what is often believed, stress does not actually derive directly from external causes, but is to a large extent self-generated. Situations are not in themselves stressful, it is our reactions which make them so.

As already mentioned, stress can mean quite different things to different people, depending on personality type – that almost indefinably subtle product of genetic conditioning, physical constitution, childhood upbringing and a host of other factors. Thus an ambitious, driving personality will most likely react quite differently from a placid, easy-going type, or a very sensitive or even anxious type, to an identical situation such as meeting a deadline, giving a public address, meeting new people at a party, handling a disagreement, attending an interview, taking an examination, and so on. Any of these very common situations may seem a stimulating challenge to one personality type, but something to be dreaded and avoided at all costs by another.

The capacity to cope with these and other potentially stressful situations is often described in terms of *stress levels*. Everyone has a personal stress level, best measured by the individual personality's ability to cope with change in life and personal circumstances, by self-expectation and degree of self-confidence. Whatever your personality, your resources in terms of attitudes, skills and the support you receive from others, must be adequate to cope with challenge, if you are to live life to the full. Certainly, knowing what your personal stress levels are, is another crucial step towards coping with stress.

Stress and lifestyle

To many people the most obviously stressful style of life is probably that led by a top businessman, living in the fast lane as he jets around the world dealing with a wide range of overtly pressured situations, involving crucial decisions and important responsibilities. But this stress-stereotype can be misleading. In fact stress affects individuals as various as a young mother bringing up small children; a factory worker on the production line; a teacher; a middle-aged housewife; someone who has lost his

11

job. All these individuals find themselves in very different situations, but all of them can, and usually do, suffer from some degree of stress, possibly of a more damaging kind than that which affects the high-flying executive.

For example, the young mother may suffer from feelings of inadequacy in meeting the variety of demands made on her by her children, which may be intensified by a sense of isolation if she lives in an environment such as a high-rise block of flats with no facilities or easy access for children.

The factory worker, although he may have no major decisions to make or difficult challenges to meet, may suffer acutely from stress derived from the sheer repetitive monotony of the production line. He may find himself playing a purely automatic part in this unstimulating process, requiring little or no initiative, and feeling no sense of involvement or achievement in having contributed to the finished product.

The teacher will have to cope with day-to-day stress in the classroom, intensified by discipline problems and inadequate resources. Overall stress will be generated by falling staffing levels, resulting in overwork, and major curriculum changes requiring a high degree of adjustment. Both may combine to create stressful feelings of lowered esteem and vocational uncertainty.

After devoting many years of her life to children who have now left home, the housewife may find herself alone in middle age with a round of unfulfilling household tasks and a husband whose own interests and job take up all his attention, with little left for her. Unless she is capable of taking a long hard look at her situation, and of developing genuinely absorbing interests of her own, neither of which she may be necessarily equipped to do, she may find herself incapable of adapting to these changes in her life, which may well be compounded at this particular time by the changes of the menopause; the cumulative frustration of her situation may cause her a very considerable degree of stress.

Finally, the man who has lost his job, possibly with little immediate prospect of finding another, will very likely be suffering from the kind of stress associated with empty days, loss of sense of direction and purpose, lowered self-esteem and a general feeling of being in a dead-end situation.

Stress and uncertainty

Sometimes stress may have no readily apparent cause. Instead, it may be linked to feelings of uncertainty, suspense and apprehension, and the unpleasant negative responses and sense of frustration that these can bring. Many people, when asked to give their idea of a stressful situation, will describe one to which they are unable to see an answer or find a way out of. For example, the terrifying uncertainty created by the nuclear threat can be truly described as one of life's greatest stressors.

Stress is not the same as pressure, although pressure can contribute to the creation of stress. A pressured situation can be rewarding, even enjoyable in terms of the extra effort, resourcefulness, organization and concentration it demands, *provided you can see your way out of it.*

Keys to stress management

The key to managing stress successfully is finding the right balance for you in the alarms-and-response system which is what stress is all about. But the following 20 basic ground rules will act as a useful framework within which you can learn to get stress into perspective.

■ Learn to appreciate the potential value of stress in creating incentive and sense of purpose, which we all need in our lives.

■ Get to know yourself and become fully aware of your personality type.

■ Remember that stress is caused from within and can be best dealt with from within.

■ Be aware of your own stress levels.

■ Learn to identify the various sources of stress inherent in your own particular lifestyle.

■ Be aware of your reactions to different sources of stress, so that these do not take you by surprise.

■ Avoid perfectionism, when this means expecting too much of both yourself and others.

- Avoid unnecessarily provoking situations where possible.

- Avoid over-committing yourself; learn when to say 'no' without feeling guilty.

- Avoid fragmentation, which is often caused by trying to do several things at once.

- Know how to avoid causing stress to others.

- Beware of unnecessary worrying.

- Learn the value of positive thinking.

- Discover how effective a cheerful outlook can be.

- Be as sure as you can be of what your motives really are, and make sure that you are really happy with them.

- Acquire the habit of sorting out your priorities.

- Learn the art of effective delegation.

- Get into the habit of talking problems through rather than bottling them up.

- Don't forget that listening is as important as talking in effective communication.

- Learn to value physical fitness as a means to relaxation and antidote to stress, and do all you can to acquire it.

Stress and your health

Effective stress-management is crucial to your total well-being because, as indicated in the chart on page 9, unmanaged stress can take a punishing toll on the body. Diseases and ailments in which stress is medically proved to play a major part, and which for this reason are often described as *stress-induced*, include:
- high blood pressure
- heart disease
- ulcers
- headaches
- insomnia
- some forms of arthritis and asthma

14

Panic attacks, which can be especially frightening because in many ways they resemble a heart attack, are a surprisingly common physical expression of stress: the symptoms include shortness of breath, dizziness, palpitations, chest pains and excessive perspiration.

Some equally unpleasant mental manifestations of stress are:
- anxiety and depression
- severely lowered self-esteem
- forgetfulness
- loss of concentration
- proneness to accident
- chronic indecisiveness
- angry outbursts
- a variety of phobias

Stress therapy

We've seen that consciously developing the right mental attitudes is of enormous importance in protecting yourself from the harmful effects of stress. The art of relaxation is also tremendously beneficial as an antidote for stress: relaxation methods may differ, but their purpose is the same – to gain control of stress-signs and draw on inner sources of strength to achieve equilibrium. Information about mental relaxation techniques can be found in chapter 9.

Physical exercise is very important too, as a way of releasing energy and achieving relaxation; and consequent physical fitness helps you stand up to stress. Exercise also helps you keep in touch with your body and enables you to read the body signs that are indicators of stress. The subject of exercise, with suggestions for special exercises for particularly stress-prone areas, is covered in chapter 8, together with advice on diet, another area in which you can do much to prevent harmful stress.

Having seen what a wealth of stress-preventive measures is available, let's take a look at some of the major situations in all our lives where stress, with its potentially positive as well as adverse effects, is often particularly evident.

TWO

STRESS AT WORK

Work is generally acknowledged to be one of the major sources of stress, and in our competitive society of high achievers has perhaps assumed a disproportionate significance. Certainly most people spend more time at work during their working lives than they do at home. Whether we are driven by over-riding ambition or take a more relaxed attitude, work is an important preoccupation for most of us. And as most work involves more or less repeated routines, drawing on a certain set of skills, in interaction with a certain group of colleagues, it is not difficult to see why potential causes of stress easily accumulate in the work place.

However, work also offers many opportunities to channel stress towards positive ends in a constructive way. Indeed this fact can sometimes be abused by companies who actually encourage stress in their employees, as a spur to achievement: the 'stress is good for you' syndrome, characteristic of the way many Japanese and American companies, in particular, work. But on a less extreme level, as well as providing a means of earning a living by one's own efforts, work also offers stimulation and, often, social activity and contacts in the form of relations with colleagues. And any job, but particularly an involving, absorbing one, can relieve stress in other areas of life by providing distraction during working hours. For all these reasons, some form of work-stress can be positive and valuable.

Changes and uncertainties at work

In the last chapter we saw that stress is often associated with change and uncertainty, and this is especially relevant in the work place. Major changes at work, like a merger or take-over or other fundamental reorganization, may all too often bring job losses without consultation, and these, together with the threat of redundancy – especially if sustained over a prolonged period – are considered to be among the most commonly encountered stressors in the work place. So are poor systems of communication and coordination, which more than anything else serve to create uncertainty.

Even if you feel secure in your job, your work may cause you stress in other ways. The desire to progress up the ladder of your career or chosen profession is a natural one, but our acutely success-conscious society, where people are not only required to be successful, but to be seen to be so, can make what should be a defined progression through a series of transitions into a highly stress-charged experience. For example, the fear of being over-looked or passed by, of not achieving a sought-after promotion, can become an over-riding preoccupation to the point of obsession; an inhibiting factor rather than a healthy incentive. Just as bad, too, can be receiving a promotion about which you feel uncertain and unable to cope with.

Other sources of stressful insecurity at work may include uncertainty about how you are rated by those to whom you are answerable, about your own specific area of responsibility, or uncertainty in the form of major, fundamental doubts about your own suitability for the job you are doing – all compounded by an overall uncertainty about how to resolve these problems.

External pressures

Most jobs are more or less directly subjected to external pressures in some form: for example, meeting an order from a possibly unreasonably demanding customer; making a presentation to a difficult client; working in the service industries and professions where there is a great deal of contact with the public. Such jobs, many of which involve extra-stressful peak periods, are often rated as especially stressful, dealing as they do with constant demands and sometimes unreasonable complaints. In all these job situations where an individual or company outside your own place of work is the potential source of stress, your success in coping will be judged largely in terms of how well you adapt to external needs and demands.

Internal pressures

In many jobs, however, stress is created by pressures from within. These will often generate from a network of working relationships: do you get on well with your colleagues? Do you know how to handle your boss? Do you relate successfully to your employees? If the answer to any of these questions is a negative one, then you have succeeded in pinpointing a potential major source of stress; and since everyone working in a business organization – even the chairman – has to relate to and answer to somebody else, stress deriving from inadequate working relationships and communications will be fairly evenly distributed throughout the work hierarchy.

Environmental stress at work

Pleasant, comfortable surroundings in which you can operate to the best of your ability contribute a lot to a stress-free working atmosphere. Considerable stress at work can be caused by the following:

- drab surroundings
- dirty conditions
- out-dated or poorly serviced machinery or equipment
- poor light
- inadequate ventilation
- too high or too low temperature
- malfunctioning air-conditioning
- over-crowding
- lack of privacy
- unacceptable noise levels
- polluted atmosphere
- poor security
- inadequate staff facilities

Most people will have worked in places where some at least of these environmental factors will be immediately recognizable. In fact they usually occur in combination, and so can have a multiple effect stresswise.

Employers are bound by the regulations of the Health and

Safety at Work Act, which covers many of these points, and it is part of good management to identify and take action upon any environmental causes of stress to staff. It is also up to individual employees, most usefully through a staff association or similar employee organization, to bring to the employer's attention points arising out of working conditions which may impair safety and optimum performance. This could result in improvements such as a no-smoking policy; well-designed and reasonably sound-proof open plan office systems; efficient security on the office building; a better standard of food and service in the canteen.

Employees under stress

A number of special stressors can arise in the employee situation. Obviously they will vary according to type of job, but the following are among the most common.

Understaffing: this can cause considerable stress if, as a result, employees find themselves over-extended, with an unacceptable workload, and sometimes doing the job of two people.

Inadequate training: too often insufficient thought is given to specific training for a particular job, both initially and on an updating basis, especially when this might mean prolonged absence from the place of work on a residential course, for example, or day-release on a regular basis over an extended period. Or else there may not be sufficient time to spare within the work organization for proper in-house training. However, this is a very false economy from the management's point of view, and can impose considerable unnecessary stress and strain on the employee.

Shift-work: this often involves unsociable hours which can create a stressful sense of disorientation, playing havoc with sleep patterns, social life and relationships, especially if shift hours are suddenly changed.

Poor management: uncommunicative and inconsiderate management can leave employees suffering from stress caused by uncertainty about their own role definition and contribution to the overall direction of the organization for which they work.

Difficult or incompetent boss: a boss of this kind is a very common cause of stress. A difficult boss will usually give insufficient direction but will expect results none the less, and will react unreasonably if he or she does not get them. An incompetent boss is often guilty of hiding behind his employees' mistakes instead of taking responsibility for them; over-delegating without giving due credit; or even attempting to pass off his or her own mistakes by laying them at the employees' door. Most people will have had some experience of this type of boss – very stressful both on a day-to-day basis and in the long term.

Workaholic boss: dealing with the type who stays in the office till 8 p.m. and expects you to do the same is stressful.

Too much or too little to do: either of these conditions can cause stress in its own way.

Relations with colleagues: these can be tricky to handle at the best of times, especially in a competitively charged working atmosphere, and if you are feeling stressed yourself you will undoubtedly affect those around you. This is one of the characteristics of stress in the work place – just one or two stressed individuals can generate further stress 'ripples' to a quite extraordinary degree.

Office politics: these offer one of the best examples of just how double-edged stress can be. 'Politics' are to a greater or lesser degree inevitable wherever you work, but how you react depends very much on your personality type. Office politics are meat and drink to some people, but cause very real stress problems to others, even to the extent of preventing them from doing their job properly.

Job dissatisfaction: always stressful, job dissatisfaction may arise for a number of reasons: you may not find your job sufficiently – or even at all – rewarding in itself; far from involving you, it may leave you at the end of the working day wondering what you have achieved. You may find that your job is so broken up and fragmented through the way you are required to do it, or from pressures of overwork, that you never really find time to enjoy it. Or you may not be able to see it leading anywhere – the 'dead end' situation can be unpleasantly stressful, often manifesting itself in feelings of chronic tiredness.

Disappointments: almost everyone suffers at least one major disappointment in the course of their working life. Learning how to handle disappointment, by putting it in its proper context, getting it in perspective and realizing it will usually be only a temporary setback that can be overcome, is one of the most constructive ways of coming to terms with a major cause of stress at work.

Causes of stress at work obviously vary from person to person and from job to job. Filling in the questionnaire on page 23 may help you to identify these in your own job, and to gauge your personal work stress levels. This simple assessment exercise may enable you to come to terms with the special sources of stress that affect you, before they become problems.

Employee's keys to coping with stress

A lot of damaging stress can be pre-empted if you know what is expected of you in your job. To make sure that you do, bear the following in mind:

Job description: a clearly defined, sufficiently detailed description of exactly what your job consists of is one of the best ways of avoiding the uncertainty which can so often lead to stress. Many people find job interviews notoriously stressful: practising the deep-breathing exercise to be found on pages 90–1 just beforehand will help, and so will having a few prepared questions ready to ask. One of these should be whether a written job description will be available, and you should make it clear that you would like one. Don't be put off by vague responses along the lines of 'The job is still developing': make it clear that you too will be developing – in the job – and you want to make sure that this will be along the right lines. Also, make sure that your job description is brought up to date as necessary, for example, if your responsibilities change.

Feedback: make sure that you get feedback on your performance and anything else you may need to know that affects your job, on a *regular* basis, from the person to whom you are answerable. If you face an end-of-year assessment, make this less of a stress hazard by making sure that you are aware in advance of the major criteria according to which your performance will be judged.

Reporting back: be clear from the start about how much your boss will expect you to do on your own initiative, and how much he or she will want you to consult with him or her. This is really all about defining the extent of your own responsibilities and it is very important, for an ideally stress-free working relationship, that both of you should be thinking along the same lines. Regular discussions with your boss are obviously valuable for you both, although the facility of 'free and frank discussion' is probably most effective when not over-used or abused.

Resilience: one of the best guide-lines for minimizing stress at work is to learn not to take things personally – not always easy, especially for sensitive, 'thin-skinned' types, but undoubtedly the source of a first-class protective coating against the wear and tear of stress. Learn to accept constructive criticism, and don't be put off by colleagues' attempts to undermine you – failure to register a reaction to these is one of the most effective ways of putting a stop to them altogether. And if your boss seems abrupt or offhand at times, remember, it is most likely nothing to do with you – he or she is probably just having a hard day.

Communication: stress feelings always intensify if they are bottled up, and this is as true at work as anywhere else. Ordinary work problems will be defused before they become damagingly stressful if you can get into the habit of talking them through with the right people: at home with your family (without overdoing it and taking the job home too often); with colleagues whom you know by experience to be trustworthy (respecting confidences is one of the

Assessing the causes of stress
SAMPLE STRESS AUDIT

How satisfied are you with:

	1 Extremely dissatisfied	2 Very dissatisfied	3 Moderately dissatisfied	4 Not sure	5 Moderately satisfied	6 Very satisfied	7 Extremely satisfied
1 The physical work conditions?							
2 The freedom to choose your own method of working?							
3 Your fellow workers?							
4 The recognition for good work?							
5 The supervision you receive?							
6 The amount of responsibility you are given?							
7 Your rate of pay?							
8 Your opportunity to use your abilities?							
9 Your chance of promotion?							
10 The way your organization is managed?							
11 The attention paid to suggestions you make?							
12 Your hours of work?							
13 The amount of variety in your work?							
14 Your job security?							
15 The training you receive?							
16 Relationships in your office/department/section?							
17 The quality of relationships between your department and other departments?							
18 Now taking everything into consideration how do you feel about your job as a whole?							

✓ | Please tick the appropriate box

During the past month, how much of the time has the job made you feel:

	1 All of the time	2 Most of the time	3 Some of the time	4 Occasionally	5 Never
1 Lively?					
2 Calm?					
3 Keen?					
4 Miserable?					
5 Lifeless?					
6 Depressed?					
7 Tense?					
8 Relaxed?					
9 Irritable?					
10 Comfortable?					
11 Lacking energy?					
12 Sleepy?					
13 Frustrated?					
14 Enthusiastic?					
15 Anxious?					
16 Gloomy?					
17 Stressed?					

What is the most satisfying aspect of your job? ....

What is the most stressful aspect of your job? ....

most constructive ways of ensuring a stress-free working atmo-sphere); and in particular with friends and acquaintances who work in similar jobs.

Physical conditions: do everything you can to make sure your personal working environment is comfortable and efficient.

■ If you spend long periods of your working day seated, your chair should support you in a comfortable position and be in the right relation to your desk height to enable you to read, write, type and word-process without experiencing any back-ache or shoulder or neck pain – all notoriously stress-prone areas.

■ VDUs can cause eye-strain, so make sure you have received adequate instruction in its use, and take special precautions on resting and relaxing your eyes (see page 90).

■ Be as well organized as possible with filing systems and desk drawers, and leave a tidy desk when you go home at night, to give you a stress-free start next day. Whatever your immediate work space, keep it free of clutter.

■ If your working day is spent on your feet, make sure you relax during your breaks in an environment that is kept clean and tidy and that you sit down and eat properly at lunchtime to help you unwind.

Executive stress

Two of the most common causes of stress to people working in an executive or managerial capacity come in one instance from above and in the other from below. The source of stress in the first instance concerns management style: the manager needs to feel that his or her own style – autocratic or relaxed, directive or participatory, to put it at its simplest – is in tune with the style of the company. If it is not, a potentially stressful element is present from the very start. The second source of stress, this time from below, concerns the realization that 'the buck stops here', which can be a profoundly isolating sensation. In a sense, a manager is really only as good as his or her relations with the staff on whom the achievement of required results depends; if these are inadequate, then the knowledge of final responsibility may bring with it the kind of sensation of panic so often associated with stress.

Another important source of executive stress is time pressure – the way he or she is expected to deal with constant interruptions and demands: telephone calls, meetings, correspondence, visitors, and so on. Again, these can come from both above and below, in the form of unrealistic expectations or contradictory demands from superiors, or an unremitting stream of questions and problems presented by subordinates. Unless a manager is well organized and equipped, the result may be a frustrating sense of fragmentation, which can easily lead to stress, especially if resources in the form of budgetary allowance and staffing levels are inadequate.

Executive keys to coping

Management training: ensure that your company provides you with the kind of comprehensive training which will enable you to organize efficiently, distribute workloads evenly, and get the most out of your staff. This is particularly important if you have risen through the ranks of the company in which you are now a manager: the assumption is all too easily made that because you are so familiar with the way the company works, you will experience no difficulties in your new role. Ensure that you do not simply receive token initial training, but that this continues through your working life, helping you to keep up with changing requirements in the market place.

Communication systems: develop these to ensure that your department members fully understand the objectives and policies in which you are all participating, and are made to feel consulted. Regular departmental meetings, sometimes of an informal nature over a Friday evening drink, are a good way of achieving this.

Delegation: skilful delegation is essential to managing time well, getting priorities right, and avoiding unnecessary stress. Equally essential to the delegation process is making sure that those to whom you delegate know exactly what it is that they are expected to do.

Acknowledgment: give credit where credit is due. Failure to do so is common and can contribute substantially towards feelings of stress in the work place.

Visibility: make sure that you are accessible and that your staff understand that this is so. Project yourself as cooperative and open to discussion. Even inadvertently isolating yourself can cause stress to both you and to others.

Listening: listening is an important aspect of the good communications which can do so much to defuse damaging stress. Make sure you listen carefully to the ideas and views you should encourage employees to put forward – they are likely to convey crucial aspirations and frustrations, which you would do well to know about.

Listen with consideration, too, to personal problems which employees may wish to discuss with you. You should welcome such an opportunity to be informed, as such problems may well affect job performance. And a sympathetic ear from the boss when required may do a great deal to help the employee's attempts to come to terms with stress.

Loyalty: be loyal to employees, as you would wish them to be loyal to you. Respect confidences, and stand up for employees' interests when necessary, to create the kind of reassurance that is one of the best protections against adverse stress.

Assertiveness: keep a high profile by learning to steer a middle course between over-assertiveness – usually not far from aggression – on the one hand, and passivity – easily misunderstood for weakness – on the other. Project yourself as fair and straightforward, and avoid both head-on confrontations or attempts to sweep things under the carpet.

Timing: a lot of stress is generated by working against the clock. Try to avoid attending meetings without giving yourself time to get properly briefed first, or cutting it uncomfortably fine when arriving at the airport for a flight.

Self-control: you will do a lot to reduce stress levels in both yourself and others by maintaining a determined, unpanicked demeanour. Try to keep tension signals at bay at all costs – they're infectious!

Disappointments: if you have reached executive level, the likelihood is that work has assumed considerable importance in your life: there could even be a danger of it assuming excessive importance. So if you have to take what may seem a step sideways rather than up on to the next rung of the ladder, try to see this as a salutary reminder that the job is important but it isn't everything – and your worth as a human being need not necessarily be judged in work terms.

Sense of balance: dealing with stress often involves sorting out your priorities. Make sure that your home life is a priority with you – it's precious, and does not deserve to be undermined by the stress of work. In fact, a good home life provides the best antidote of all to damaging stress – so work on it too.

Working women under stress

Unfortunately, despite all that they have achieved for themselves, women are still too often discriminated against in a work context – often indirectly, but the effects can be as damaging as if it were overtly. Women are still having to fight for acceptance in professions still overwhelmingly dominated by men. They may have to prove themselves extra hard, and may encounter disturbing and stressful levels of hostility, prejudice, sexism and harassment.

As the number of women achieving executive status increases, so, perhaps predictably, but significantly, does the incidence of stress-related illness in women. In general, women are too often still paid less than men, or are given jobs which do not carry sufficient security. Women still encounter tremendous difficulties in fulfilling the dual role of maintaining a home as well as working outside it, with concomitant feelings of anxiety and guilt. There is more about the stressful implications of such a situation in the next chapter.

Useful steps which women can take to ensure that they are subjected to minimum special stress at work include first and foremost some reorganization of home and childcare to ensure that the two sides of life run together as smoothly as possible. It would be wise, too, to find out as much as possible about any prospective employer in terms of attitudes towards maternity leave and equal opportunities. And to find out whether the company provides creche facilities, or could be persuaded to do so.

Deadlines

Most people have to meet deadlines at some time or other, at a variety of work levels. Whether they form an habitual part of a job, or occur only infrequently, deadlines impose special stresses.

The best initial approach to a deadline is to look at it positively: as with any potentially stressful activity, positive thinking can achieve a great deal. Get into the habit of seeing a deadline as a target, a means of achievement. Cope with more complex deadlines by breaking them down into smaller stages and allocating a time span to each. Establish the order of priorities, and draw up a realistic schedule accordingly, if possible maintaining a degree of flexibility in order to cope with unforeseen contingencies. And if you are sharing the meeting of a deadline, for example in a team situation, make sure that everyone involved knows the priorities and is aware of the schedule and his or her individual part in it.

Workaholics

Workaholics create special stresses for themselves and for those with whom they come into contact – their work colleagues and their families. Workaholism is itself a striking symptom of stress; it may have developed as a result of overwork, so that this becomes habitual, or as a means of escape from other forms of stress, such as difficult personal relationships or an unsatisfactory home life. Whichever, workaholics are highly stressed and stressful people who most often cause stress at home by their prolonged absences or lack of involvement, and at work by expecting too much of colleagues or employees who are unable or unwilling to work at the same hectic pace.

If you detect signs in yourself that indicate you may be developing this sort of attitude towards your work, remind yourself that there is a big difference between finding a job so fulfilling and rewarding that you are prepared to give a great deal of your time to it, and using work as a substitute for or an escape from other equally or more important things in life. Remind yourself, too, that working round the clock is not a sign of efficiency, and may be unfair on others, causing problems of resentment.

Keys to health at work

Holidays: maintaining a healthy balance in your life is a highly constructive way of tackling the problem of stress at work. Holidays, for example, play an important part in compensating for hard work throughout the year, and should not be overlooked. Don't leave taking a holiday for too long, as you will need that much longer to unwind while you are on holiday. Holidays have very real value when it comes to preventing stress from becoming harmful; there is more about this in chapter 4. Make best use of weekends as well as annual holidays, to recharge your batteries regularly.

Exercise: this is extremely important for physical relaxation and releasing and channelling energy effectively: it is covered in detail in chapter 8. Your work will benefit if you make a point of taking regular exercise, and make it complement the type of work you do. For example, if your job is a sedentary one indoors, you will certainly benefit from exercise in the fresh air – even building a daily walk into your working day will help.

If you work amid high noise levels, you may find some of the relaxation techniques described in chapter 9, as well as a restful activity like listening to soothing music, particularly beneficial.

Diet: watch your diet too. Avoid hastily snatched pub lunches, and excessively heavy eating and drinking in the middle of the day. If you take a packed lunch to work, make sure it is healthy and varied. A stress-free diet and a healthy heart are discussed in chapter 8.

Check-ups: pay particular attention to any early warning signs of the stress-induced disorders described on pages 82–3. Have a medical check-up regularly and take full advantage of the facilities afforded by medical insurance schemes, which many companies now offer as part of their package to employees.

Losing your job

Losing a job is one of the most powerful stressors, considered by many experts to be second stress-wise only to bereavement, to which it can be compared in a number of ways. The pattern of reaction to losing a job is markedly similar to the various stages most people go through following the death of someone close to them: an initial reaction of numbed shock, disbelief, and frequently anger, followed by a period of lethargy and inertia; then, if unemployment is prolonged, a state of passive acceptance, with feelings of loss of identity, before, hopefully, coming to terms with the situation either through finding a new job or some satisfying and fulfilling alternative.

Losing a job can often involve acute financial stress if the person affected has major commitments – a mortgage and school fees, for example. It also means losing the framework within which a working life is structured, together with the network of contacts outside the home which most jobs involve, and the feeling of identity associated with the job. It can cause severe stresses and strains within marriage and family life generally, and strong feelings of personal inadequacy.

Keys to coping with unemployment

■ Help yourself deal with the sense of disorientation so often experienced by the jobless, by planning your day carefully, for example, getting up early and taking the day from there.

■ Make every effort to look, and keep looking, for a job. Even if no opportunities arise immediately for the type of work for which you are qualified, it may be wise to consider alternative types of job, if available – perhaps on a part-time basis to be going on with – on the premise that it is usually easier to find the right job if you are already employed, as well as being good for the morale and the budget.

- Use the extra leisure time available to you constructively. Instead of regarding it as a bane, think of it as an opportunity that has never arisen before for developing new interests and skills – ideally in the company of others, to maintain social contact and avoid isolation – and also to give you an added string to your bow in your search for work.

- Get out of the house as much as possible.

- Keep as fit as possible.

Self-employed stress

Being your own boss offers unique opportunities for genuine job satisfaction, and for many people a blessed release from hassle from the boss, and office politics. But self-employment can create its own set of stress factors, and it is wise to be aware of these before taking the step to self-employment, to be sure that your stress levels are going to be able to cope. To be successfully self-employed, you have to be self-sufficient, and extra-disciplined and well-organized.

Working for yourself can be an isolating business, and feelings of isolation can be notoriously stressful. There is always the temptation to overwork, in itself another of the major stressors – saying no to work is one of the most difficult decisions for any self-employed person – and if you are a one-man firm you will have no one to whom you can delegate.

It helps to have a reasonably buoyant personality, to be optimistic and positive, not too much of a worrier. You need to take extra steps to be strict with yourself: if you work at home, to make sure that you keep your own 'office hours'; and to keep your home and work lives as separate as reasonably possible.

Illness, often itself a major cause of stress, can be especially stressful to the self-employed. You will not benefit from sick pay unless you have taken out insurance to cover the possibility of extended periods off work through illness, and it is worth investigating these.

Cash flow problems are often a bugbear for self-employed people, and one of the best ways of all of avoiding financial stress is to get yourself a really good accountant with a genuine interest in the type of work you will be asking him to do for you.

Stress management at work

Fortunately, business companies are becoming increasingly aware of the problems stress can cause their employees, and are looking at ways to deal with these. A useful booklet, *Action on Stress at Work*, which is published by the Health Education Authority, outlines practical ways of reducing stress at work from an employer's point of view, and gives an action plan for tackling stress at organizational level: setting up an action group, assessing the current situation by means of a stress audit; tackling taboos; looking at stress-related factors like working days lost through sickness and strikes, accidents at work, excessive drinking and smoking in employees; formulating, implementing and monitoring a stress policy. The booklet examines in detail the use of stress counselling by companies, using the In-House Counselling Scheme at the GPO as an illustration of how this can work.

Many foundations and associations concerned with stress offer special facilities for handling it in the workplace. For example, the Yoga Health Foundation (details in chapter 10) holds stress-management courses for the welfare officers of the various Civil Service departments at its residential centre in Bedfordshire.

Films and videos can be useful aids for getting the stress message across in a work context. Two such are *Stress at Work*, which looks at the experiences and ideas of people who have had to cope with too much work pressure, featuring interviews with a catering manager, secretary, bus mechanic, airline ticket clerk, social worker and shop steward: available from Concord Films, 201 Felixstowe Road, Ipswich, Suffolk, 1P39BJ. Tel. 0473 726012; and *Stress: Recognizing the Causes*, a video focusing on an industrial manager: available from Video Arts, 68 Oxford Street, London W1. Tel: 01-637 7288.

THREE

STRESS AT HOME

The value of a secure and happy home life as a safeguard against harmful stress cannot be overestimated. A stable, supportive home atmosphere in which problems can be discussed as they arise will probably do more than anything else to prevent them from becoming stressful.

Unfortunately, however, the demands of daily life are such that this is by no means always feasible, and all too often the home itself can become an arena for some of the most stressful conflicts of all. These can arise for a host of reasons, among the most common being marital differences; sexual difficulties (see page 93); problems with children; money worries; disagreements with in-laws; and combining a job and home life – which can be one of the all-time great juggling acts!

Marital stress

For many people, despite the high divorce rate, marriage is still the most significantly supportive and confiding relationship, one which provides the kind of framework that makes it possible to overcome all kinds of difficulties, and negotiate all sorts of changes elsewhere in life.

Yet causes for conflict in marriage are seemingly infinite, ranging as they do from the very obvious to the seemingly totally trivial. Expectations placed on marriage may be unrealistic, or they may not coincide.

Possibly one of the most fundamental sources of stress between married couples (like many other forms of stress) is connected to change. People change, and when there are two of you, it may not always be in the same direction. Expectations of life and of each other, aspirations, the priorities and shared interests which formed the common ground on which the marriage was built in the first place, may diverge gradually over a period of time, perhaps almost imperceptibly, until differences finally emerge into the open and uncertainty, another major stressor, takes over.

To be aware of the possibility of such a pattern developing in your marriage, and to take preventive steps in time, can save you a lot of stress in your life. Any form of isolation can be stressful, and feeling isolated within marriage must rate especially high on the stress scale. Making time for each other, especially in the face of taxing demands from work and children, can often be one of the soundest premises for a stress-free marriage. And so, on the other hand, can a certain degree of independence – realizing, for instance, that just because you are married you may not necessarily always enjoy identical interests or share exactly the same friends.

The dual-career marriage

Marriages in which both partners work are increasingly common, a fact which may in itself be a partial answer to why so many marriages also suffer from stress and run into trouble.

A working husband and wife have much to offer each other: apart from increased relief from financial pressures which a dual income brings, they will both have more to talk about apart from principal common interests like home and children. Very importantly, each partner will be aware of the kind of stress the other may undergo from time to time at work, by being able to identify with the problem through shared work experience.

However, the stressful side of the dual-career situation arises when work interferes with the quality of home life. Tired at the end of a working day, perhaps neither partner will have the inclination to talk or listen to each other, or their children; there is just not enough time or energy to enjoy being at home to the full.

Significantly, although career couples are expected to have more egalitarian values than those where the wife does not work, household tasks still tend to be unevenly distributed: it is estimated that 65 per cent of married women in Britain work, but a recent survey indicates that 73 per cent of women do nearly all the housework, an inequal division easily capable of turning into a stressful issue.

Stress between a husband and wife who both work can also become particularly acute if the work itself causes feelings of rivalry or resentment. This is a very common state of affairs if the wife earns more than the husband, or if she has gone back to work or taken a job after a number of years at home. Jobs change people, and new interests, contacts, and increased self-confidence in a working wife may be reflected in feelings of inadequacy and insecurity in her husband.

Keys to coping for the working wife

■ Try to be aware of problems that may arise in your relationship through combining a job with running a home, before they catch up on you. It's sometimes easier to recognize this well-known source of stress in others than in yourself! Make a point of talking through difficulties together *before* they become hostile issues.

■ Try not to let your working and home lives overlap. As far as possible avoid taking family worries to work and bringing the job home. Instead, use each of your two lives as a means of relieving stress in the other.

■ Encourage your partner by being a good listener and proffering advice as and when appropriate, but avoid even indirect pressuring – this can sometimes be quite unconscious – which can easily cause additional stress.

■ Make use of self-help organizations such as the Working Mothers' Association (see chapter 10) to combine life at work and at home successfully.

■ Try to set aside some time, however short, in which to relax when you get home from work, to make the transition smoother. If you can possibly sit down for 10 minutes when you get in before preparing the evening meal, you'll feel a lot better for it. You may also find the following tips useful:

12 tips for minimizing household stress

The ideal of material success beloved of the media, and now a more or less fundamental requirement of our consumer society, is not only responsible for much stress at work; it affects home life too. Competitiveness is a strong motivator, but by inviting comparisons with other people's situations can also be responsible for a great deal of harmful stress. The very natural desire to create pleasant surroundings in the home, and to run it smoothly and efficiently, is exploited quite ruthlessly by the advertising industry, very often by use of the 'keeping up with the Joneses' principle. The home, which should be one of life's great pleasures, can all too easily become a source of dissatisfaction and a hotbed of stress instead. Trying too hard to live up to what the media tell us we want and should expect of ourselves is one of the most common causes of stress in many people's lives. The adjustment between what you feel you are actually capable of – or what you can afford – and what you feel you should aspire to, can be painful or even impossible, and the cause of quite unreasonable feelings of inadequacy, envy and resentment. The following pointers are designed to help you avoid these as far as possible.

■ Don't be too much of a perfectionist. Home is a place to live in. It's always entertaining to look at other people's living spaces as featured in glossy magazines, for example, and these are often great sources of ideas for decorating or furnishing your own home, but trying to create an identically immaculate home environment in real life can be just another way of building up stress for yourself.

■ Get your priorities right. Draw up a list of the things that really matter most to you in your home life, discuss these with the other people you share it with, make any necessary adjustments and use the result as a working guide for unstressed everyday living.

■ Share responsibilities, and make sure each person involved knows what these are: for example, who pays the household bills, who makes sure the dustbins get taken out on collection days, whose turn it is to cook.

■ Share household chores like cleaning, shopping and cooking. Very few people can honestly say they enjoy housework, but dividing it up sensibly, so that one person is responsible for hoovering once a week, say, another for cleaning the kitchen and bathroom, makes it much less of a drag. And a home that is kept reasonably clean and tidy is more relaxing to be in, and can do a lot to relieve stressful feelings in other areas.

■ Shopping, too, benefits from sharing. Many people find a big weekly shop at the supermarket the most economical way of stocking up. Well-run and designed supermarkets, with clearly identified aisles and plenty of room to move between them, make shopping an easier and pleasanter experience: if you can shop at off-peak times – avoiding Saturday mornings for example – and if there are two of you, one to offload and one to pack, you can take a lot of the stress out of queuing up at the check-out till. Obviously, avoiding taking very young children with you keeps the shopping stress levels down, as can writing out a well-thought out list beforehand – this does away with indecision and dithering when faced with a barrage of supermarket choices, which can be stressful.

■ Cooking, which should be a pleasure, is much less likely to become a chore on a day-to-day basis if you share it, perhaps alternating evening meals during the week if you both work, and doing some more inventive cooking together at weekends.

■ Learn to delegate: delegating appropriately rather than trying to do everything yourself is a sure way of cutting back on stress, and skilful delegation also means that the whole family will acquire valuable survival skills.

■ On the same principle, encourage children to help. Sell them ideas rather than nagging at them: for example, explain that if they retain responsibility for tidying their own rooms on a reasonably regular basis, they will know for themselves exactly where everything is kept and will not have to waste their time (and yours) by asking.

■ Labour-saving devices can take a lot of stress out of running a home, although this doesn't mean you have to buy every gadget in sight! Instead, choose equipment that will best help you with jobs that need to be done on a regular basis: for example, a dishwasher means not only that you won't need to waste valuable time at the sink, but also helps keep the kitchen clear of accumulated washing-up. A good-sized freezer means that you can keep a supply of pre-cooked dishes ready for emergencies or those times when you're so tired that cooking a meal from scratch seems too much like a stressful ordeal. Certainly a well-designed and fitted kitchen can be an invaluable practical aid to coping with domestic stress.

■ Even if you can't always eat together because of different timetables, make sure you get together for meals regularly as opportunities for conversation, talking about things of interest and concern to all the family, and generally keeping in touch.

■ For the same reasons, try to make sure the whole family shares some leisure activity, such as a combined trip to the local swimming pool once a week, or a walk or picnic at weekends.

■ Finally, always try to get off to a good start in the morning – prime time for stress in many families! For example, if you share one bathroom, make sure this is done on a simple rota basis. Or if packed lunches are required by some members of the family, try to get these ready the night before.

Stress with children

Bringing up children is certainly one of the most rewarding experiences, but also one of the most exhausting full-time jobs imaginable if you are coping with their incessant demands 24 hours a day. Children develop amazingly quickly, and keeping up with – let alone adjusting to – their changing needs, can be a highly stressful business.

Caring for children can also lead to a special kind of isolation in which stress very easily builds up, particularly if you live in an area where facilities for children are not readily accessible, and if you have to rely on public transport or take a baby and toddler along with you to the supermarket. Anyone who has experienced the difficulties of getting pushchairs and children simultaneously on and off buses, or pushed a shopping trolley round a crowded supermarket while trying to control young children at the same time, knows just how stressful it is, and how tempting it can be to stay at home with the children – but that can be just when things get harmfully stressful.

Coping with childhood illnesses, too, and difficulties at school, about which there's more in chapter 6, can be every bit as stressful for parents as for children.

Keys to coping at home with children

There's some special advice on dealing with the stress of a new baby in chapter 5, but there are plenty of things you can do to go on keeping stress at bay as your children grow older, and prevent it from damaging your relationship with them and your enjoyment of watching them grow up.

■ Do all you can to make your home childproof. Every year one in five children has an accident at home that is serious enough to require medical treatment, and the vast majority of these occur between the age when a baby starts to crawl, and about 4 years, by which time most children will have learnt to recognize the major dangers around them. During this time when children are especially vulnerable, as they indulge their natural curiosity and explore their surroundings, while still innocent of the fear which acts as a natural brake, you can make life safer for them as well as less stressful for yourself by taking some simple yet effective precautions:

□ In the kitchen, fit your cooker and hobs with special guards. Some ovens feature special childproof switches. Make sure flexes on kettles and other kitchen equipment are carefully coiled, not hanging over the work surface, and that saucepan handles on top of the stove are turned away from the edge, well out of reach.

□ In the bathroom, make sure that the medicine cabinet is locked, or fitted with a child-resistant catch.

□ Gates and barriers on the stairs will prevent falls.

□ A playpen is invaluable for ensuring that your child is safe and happy during those moments when you are busy and cannot give him or her all your attention. An easily portable playpen is most useful.

□ All the windows in the house should be fitted with locks, and all fires and heaters protected by guards.

□ Keep precious knick-knacks high up well out of reach.

■ Get out as much as you can with your children: join a mother and toddler group; make shopping easier by going with a friend; join a car pool when the children get to school age.

■ Try to avoid the all-too-common stress situation that can arise when the children seem to have taken over completely. Watch out for this: keep part of your life separate from children, to listen to what your partner's day was like, however much you may be longing to let off steam about yours, and make sure that he gets to share in the fun of childcare as well as some of the chores. And if you can possibly arrange it, do your best to get out together on your own fairly regularly, and even away on a few days' holiday by yourselves from time to time.

Help at home

Reliable help at home, if you can afford it, can be a god-send for keeping stress levels down. You can be sure that the superwomen we would all like to emulate, combining a successful, high-powered job with happy children and a well-run home, and still with time left over for effortless entertaining, are not just well-organized people, but have help they know they can count on.

However, whether the help is a baby-sitter, daily (or occasional cleaner), or part-time nanny, or a live-in au pair, it is essential that both sides – the helper and the helped – should understand exactly what the duties involved are, and make sure that time off, for example, is not abused. And if your home help is specifically there to look after the children, it is vital that you should feel that relations with the children themselves are all you would wish. Otherwise help can become stressful in its own right.

A word about help from parents and in-laws. Parents often want to help, by baby-sitting, taking the grandchildren for the day while you are out, or even for longer periods to enable you to get a well-deserved holiday. It's lovely for everybody when this works out – an integrated extended family unit is itself protection against a number of stresses in family life, and is becoming all too rare here, compared with Mediterranean and Asian countries where it is very much still the norm. But kind offers of help from this source should not be abused, and are perhaps best thought of on an occasional basis, although obviously this will differ according to family circumstances. Parent–child relations don't cease to be a well-known area of stress just because you're all grown up, and if you allow parents to do too much for your children, however kindly this is meant, you may end up by regretting it. Leaving children with parents while you go on holiday may seem ideally convenient, but for older people unused to young children on a regular basis, it can be exhausting, and you may find yourself returning from a relaxing holiday only to be met with an unexpectedly stressful situation at home.

Financial stress

Money worries rate as one of the most common causes of individual stress and sources of strain and friction in relationships. For many people, the fear of not being able to manage because of the inroads of inflation is never far away. Other factors which make it difficult for people to control their money, and consequently more vulnerable to stress, are the very widespread use of plastic money and easy access to instant credit.

Keys to money management

Managing finance is a highly personal matter, but here are some basic guidelines which can help to keep financial pressures down.

- Get into the habit of budgeting carefully. Be aware of the funds you will need to have available to meet monthly and quarterly bills; keep receipts from household shopping from week to week, so that you can keep track of your outgoings on food and other items, and be in a position to make any adjustments you think necessary.

- Resist the persuasive letters sent out by companies offering credit facilities. Remember that their tone will change drastically if you get into arrears! Try to make the use of any credit cards you may have part of your general budgeting, rather than in addition to it.

- It is by no means easy to save nowadays, but if you can possibly get into the habit of putting something aside for a rainy day, you will effectively be taking out one of the best possible forms of insurance against harmful stress.

Single-parent stress

Bringing up a child or children on your own is a challenge currently being met by an increasing number of parents; it has been estimated that as many as one in five families now fall into this category. Whether you are a single parent from choice, or as the result of circumstances outside your control, the challenge, like any other, can involve a quite considerable degree of stress. Single-parenting can be isolating – no longer, fortunately, as the result of social prejudices, but simply because the single parent is thrown on his/her own resources to such an extent. He or she must make all the decisions and take all the responsibilities, with fewer chances to talk through problems or concerns with a partner. There is always the danger, too, of becoming over-dependent on your children, which can lead to problems later on, and there are usually special problems for single parents in combining a job with looking after the children: as every single parent knows, day care facilities such as company creches, all-day nursery schools and play groups, registered child-minders, are in all too short supply.

A single parent can keep stress in perspective by remembering that all these points can be applied to dual parenting as well. As seen already, bringing up children in general can be an isolating experience in some circumstances. Two parents may disagree over quite fundamental things in relation to bringing up their children – such as which schools to send them to – one problem which the single parent will never have to face. And many mothers bringing up children within a partnership can also become over-dependent on their children – sometimes unconsciously, so that they may only realize it when the children grow up and leave home.

To keep the sense of balance that prevents challenge or change from becoming stressful, try to preserve a certain degree of independence in relation to your children, and encourage the same in them. For example, take a holiday away from each other from time to time, when they are old enough, and share as many activities as possible with other family and friends. Single parents are very well served by some excellent support groups like

Gingerbread, whose services can do a lot to alleviate stress. More details of these can be found in chapter 10.

Moving house

Solicitors dealing on a day-to-day basis with clients involved in a variety of stressful situations, rate moving house as one of the most powerful of all stressors, not far below bereavement and divorce on the stress scale. Some people do of course move house more frequently than others, sometimes for work reasons, sometimes just in order to keep moving up the property ladder, and most people on average move at least two or three times in their lifetimes, but to many people, moving is real anathema, and very stressful.

Moving house undoubtedly causes stress because of the big changes it usually involves. Buying a new property is a major financial commitment, almost always costing more than antici-pated, however carefully you do your sums. Apart from the almost inevitable degree of financial stress involved, there is also the factor of departing from familiar surroundings for relatively unknown territory, which can mean leaving good neighbours behind, and in the case of children, saying goodbye to friends at school – and children, noted for their general dislike of change, will quite often resist the idea of moving to a new area very strongly.

Keys to a smooth move

For everyone involved in the move, the stressful element will not be removed until a complete adjustment has been made to the new home, and there are a number of ways in which you can make this easier for yourself in advance.

■ Get to know your new neighbourhood as well as you can before the move itself. You will probably have familiarized yourself with it while house-hunting – this is certainly advisable – but once you know your house purchase is definitely going ahead, visit the new area as often as you can before you actually move, to find out about local shops, transport, facilities for children, leisure facilities generally, and so on. If you can, find out who your new neighbours will be, and perhaps even introduce yourself in advance.

■ Plan your move carefully, to make sure it goes as smoothly as possible. You will want to get estimates for the actual cost of the move, but remember that paying a bit more for a reliable firm with a good name can pay dividends: you will be able to explain any particular requirements you may have to their experienced estimator, and will not need to waste time and nervous energy on removal day worrying whether the men will turn up.

■ Use the move positively to discard the unwanted clutter most people accumulate without realizing it, so that you can get off to a fresh start.

■ If you have young children and pets, make arrangements for them to be looked after while the move is taking place.

■ On the day itself, make sure everything is clearly labelled, showing which room in the new house it belongs to, and establish a good rapport with the removal men, who will usually gladly drink as many cups of tea as they are offered.

With just a little forethought and advance planning, moving house can be substantially de-stressed.

Taking the stress out of entertaining

Throwing a party comes totally naturally and spontaneously to some people; to others it can seem like a real ordeal, and turn into a genuinely stressful experience. Anxieties about not being able to match the standards of those whose hospitality you are returning, or being unable to meet the expectations you feel others have of you, are often the cause of becoming stressed when entertaining at home.

Keys to relaxed entertaining

Obviously, if you entertain only occasionally you are more likely to experience the kind of stressful feelings that can spoil your own party for you, but even the most experienced hosts may find it useful to bear a few pointers in mind to help keep this kind of stress to a minimum.

- As with all forms of stress management, get your priorities right from the start: the point about a party is for everybody to enjoy each other's company – and that includes the host or hostess.

- Forget about keeping up with the Joneses. Whatever type of party you have in mind, keep it simple – for example, avoid elaborate menus that involve lengthy periods in the kitchen away from your guests.

- Help yourself to stay relaxed by preparing as much as possible in advance: make maximum use of the freezer, and if you are catering for large numbers and run out of room, borrow some temporary freezer space from friends.

- Don't make the mistake of trying out a new recipe that looks a bit complicated for a party – it's much better to stick to tried and tested favourites, and experiment with new recipes when you're on your own.

- Make sure if you have invited people you don't know so well to your party that you have some old friends present too, on whom you can rely for help if necessary.

- Think about sharing a party with friends, a sure way of reducing pressure.

- Parties where guests each bring a dish can be tremendous fun, and cut right down on the stress levels.

Stress at Christmas

For a number of reasons, Christmas can often turn out to be one of the most stressful times of the year. This is very likely partly because, coming when it does, Christmas is often a time when one tends to assess the year gone by, with its disappointments as well as its achievements. Also, simply because it is the traditional season for getting together and exchanging greetings, Christmas can heighten feelings of loneliness, always a potential source of stress. But ironically, Christmas family gatherings can be notoriously stressful occasions as well, fraught with tension and friction which seem almost inevitable when family members possibly meet only once a year. And celebrating Christmas is unfortunately now such a commercial enterprise that the preparations start earlier and earlier each year, and the build-up can seem endless. It's only too easy to try to do far too much, and get tired and stressed.

One way to counter this is to be as well organized as possible, by working out a really manageable count-down well in advance, and sticking to it. Another is to stop and remind yourself what Christmas is all about, and this is when the simplest of shared preparations can often result in the most successful celebrations, with a really happy, stress-free Christmas for everyone.

Stress Rating Scale

In the late 1960s Dr Thomas Holmes and Dr Richard Rahe, of the University of Washington in Seattle, USA, published in chart form, in the *Journal of Psychosomatic Research*, the degrees of stress, based on a scale from 1 to 100, which their research showed as commonly associated with life events. Whether or not you feel your own stress levels coincide with the findings outlined in the chart, it provides a comprehensive checklist of stressors which affect us all.

	100		100
Death of spouse	100	Large mortgage or loan	31
Divorce	73	New responsibilities at work	29
Marital separation	65	Children leaving home	29
Jail term	63	Trouble with in-laws	29
Death in family	63	Outstanding personal	
Personal injury or illness	53	achievement	28
Marriage	50	Spouse begins or stops work	26
Losing a job	47	School or college ends or	
Marital reconciliation	45	begins	26
Retirement	45	Living conditions change	25
Illness of family member	44	Personal habits change	24
Pregnancy	40	Trouble with boss	23
Sex problems	39	Change in working conditions	20
New baby	39	Change in residence	20
Business readjustment	39	Change in school or college	20
Change in financial		Change in social activities	18
circumstances	38	Change in sleeping habits	16
Death of a close friend	37	Change in eating habits	15
Change in work	36	Holiday	13
Increased arguments with		Christmas	12
spouse	35	Minor violations of law	11

FOUR

HOLIDAY AND TRAVEL STRESS

A good holiday can do wonders towards mending the wear and tear of stress, recharging the batteries and helping to get everyday problems into perspective. Regular, well-chosen holidays are acknowledged to play an important role in stress-resistance, and as seen in chapter 2, it is unwise to go too long without taking a holiday.

Yet, perhaps surprisingly, holidays can equally become stressful experiences in their own right, unless you are careful. This is mainly because holidays are all about change, which consistently tends to generate stress. Holidays represent a variety of changes: a change of scene, and a chance to experience at first hand a different way of life, customs and traditions, and often changes in food, language and money as well. All of these can be highly beneficial, exposing you to a whole range of stimulating new experiences. But they have their stressful side too: unfamiliar surroundings can create feelings of disorientation and loss of control; problems with not understanding the language can be confusing and frustrating; different food may cause upsets and so on.

To avoid stress on holiday, you need to make sure that all the changes it involves add up to a valuable and refreshing, positive experience, not a stressful one.

Keys to stress-free holidays
■ Don't be too ambitious when planning your holiday. Don't allow what should be a relaxing, regenerative experience to turn into a major challenge.

■ Do plenty of homework to make sure you choose the holiday that's right for you – all of you, if you are going on holiday as a family or in a group. With many people now taking at least two holidays a year, the holiday business is one of the boom industries, and there is a wealth of holidays to choose from. But being literally spoiled for choice means you also need to choose extra-carefully. For example, if you have young children with you, you need to find out if there will be good facilities for them. If an outward-bound, adventure type of holiday attracts you, you need to be sure that you are fit enough to undertake it pleasurably. If you are not naturally gregarious, you need to think carefully about going on a cruise, however attractive the itinerary sounds. If you are looking after a family all year, a self-catering holiday may not be enough of a break, and so on.

■ Ideally, get a personal recommendation on the hotel or other accommodation you may opt for.

■ Going to the same place every year may not sound exciting, but many people, especially those with young families, find the familiarity and informality of such an arrangement offers the best way of achieving a stress-free, relaxing holiday.

■ Book the holiday through a travel agent you know and trust.

■ Be sure to take out proper insurance and make sure you understand the small print detailing exactly what it covers. Illness or accident on holiday, stressful in itself, will be more so if you find you are not adequately covered by insurance.

■ Allow yourself plenty of time to obtain visas, inoculation certificates, or whatever documents are necessary – getting these can take longer than you might expect.

■ Make sure you also order currency and travellers' cheques in plenty of time before your departure.

■ Make a list of the special holiday items you will need, and allow yourself plenty of time to buy these.

■ Try to learn at least a few useful phrases of the language of the country you will be visiting.

■ Ensure a stress-free journey by making sure that you can carry your luggage easily, and take one hold-all or case rather than an awkward assortment of smaller bags. Make a habit of travelling as light as you possibly can. Make sure, too, that you are packed in advance – say the night before departure – to avoid stressful, last-minute panics.

■ If you are travelling in your own car, make sure it has been serviced, before setting out, and that you have an international driving licence if you need one.

■ If you are travelling by air or train, allow yourself enough time to get to the airport or station comfortably.

■ Ensure peace of mind on holiday by making sure that all is properly taken care of at home.
  □ Have you arranged for the dog or cat to go into kennels?
  □ Have outstanding bills been paid? (There's nothing to send the blood pressure soaring like coming back from holiday to a pile of red final reminder notices.)
  □ Have milk and papers been cancelled?
  □ Have arrangements been made for watering the garden and house plants?
  □ Have you left a note of your itinerary and contact telephone number with a relative or trustworthy friend or neighbour?
  □ Have you turned off all appliances, lights and taps?
  □ Have doors and windows been securely locked on leaving the house?

■ To avoid stressful disappointments on holidays, go prepared for contingencies. If you are expecting constant sunshine but it rains non-stop instead, you will be able to cope better if you go well supplied with the reading you've been trying to catch up on all year, and plenty of games for the children.

■ On your return from an enjoyable and relaxing holiday, don't immediately undo all the benefits by rushing back into work, however strong the temptation may be when you're faced with piles of mail and strings of messages. It is so much better to pace yourself back into your job gradually if you can.

Keys to successful holiday sharing

When it works, sharing a holiday with friends can be great fun, but many people would agree that it can equally be a quite extraordinarily stressful experience. To make sure you come back from holiday with friends looking forward to sharing the same enjoyable experience for many years to come, rather than feeling a valued friendship has been irretrievably lost, do some hard thinking beforehand:

■ Holidays are precious, and shared holidays need an extra degree of planning to be successful.

■ If two of you are planning to go on holiday together, do you know each other well enough to be aware of each other's tastes and preferences, and to be sure that these will coincide? It's often said that there's no better way of getting to know a person than to go on holiday together – but it can be a hard way to find out more about someone!

■ If you have any serious doubts, it might be better to go on one of the increasingly popular singles holidays and meet new people in an exciting environment.

■ Two families sharing a holiday house abroad can often find this a stressful experience. This is usually because each family has its own ways of doing things, and even the smallest differences in routine can assume an unreasonable importance.

■ When there is a group of you on holiday, it's a good idea to avoid living in each other's pockets, and instead agree on a degree of friendly independence, to accommodate differences of taste such as: liking to get up late on holiday/wanting to get off to an early start; being more than happy to spend the day lounging on the beach/wanting to see all the sights. If this is properly handled, you will most likely find that everybody adapts and enjoys the holiay much more as a result.

■ Money often turns out to be a cause of particular stress on holiday, especially if it is felt that some members of the party are not paying their way. Make sure that money is sensibly yet unobtrusively organized – a simple kitty system may be best.

50

■ If you are self-catering, it may be a good idea to agree to take it in turns to cook, to make this a pleasure rather than a chore, and also to avoid conflicts in the kitchen – a notoriously stressful area!

Air travel

With holidays in far-flung and exotic places becoming increasingly popular, and the speed and convenience of air travel remaining unchallenged, more and more people are taking to the air, despite the fact that for a number of reasons flying is a specially stress-prone form of transport.

Airports are overworked places, often crowded and noisy, and can be highly confusing to those unfamiliar with them. Flight delays and cancellations, which all too frequently coincide with peak travelling times, and long drawn-out check-in, security check and baggage retrieval procedures, can all contribute substantially to the feelings of apprehension, and sometimes downright fear, which many people experience when flying. The publicity surrounding air disasters does not help in this respect, although for most people the root causes of fear of flying are phobias like terror of heights and claustrophobia, as well as the feeling of being out of control, which is commonly associated with stress generally.

Deep breathing techniques (see page 90) and other relaxation techniques, such as those described in chapter 9, can be highly beneficial during an air flight. The decompressed atmosphere in the flight cabin of the aircraft creates physical conditions which can contribute to a general feeling of stress: dehydration is one of these, and is best countered by taking in plenty of compensating fluid before and during the flight, but avoiding alcohol, caffeine and carbonated drinks, which increase the discomfort of dehydration.

Jet-lag can be a special problem as a result of long distance flights which cross through different time zones. Jet-lag disrupts our internal routines (called circadian rhythms) and forces the body clock, which works to a 24-hour cycle, out of synch. The result can feel rather like flu, with loss of energy, fatigue, poor concentration and disrupted sleep, until the body has had sufficient recovery time to re-adjust.

On long flights it is advisable to wear loose, comfortable

clothing to enable you to relax and get as much rest as you can – ear-plugs and eye masks can also be helpful – and then, on reaching your destination, try not to go to sleep until the local bedtime. It is advisable to plan your journey so that on returning home after a long-distance flight, you can allow yourself a couple of days to recover: for example, it is not a good idea to attempt to go into work the day you get back, or even the following day. Ideally, aim to return home late on a Friday, so that you can have the weekend to get rid of the physical stress of jet-lag. If you can travel really light, restricting yourself to cabin baggage, you'll avoid those stressful long waits at the carousel while luggage is unloaded from the hold of the aircraft.

Car travel

Driving at its best, when the car is going well and the open road lies ahead of you, can be a delightfully relaxing activity and do a lot to help unwind. But a number of quite clearly identifiable factors combine to make driving a high-profile stress-related activity.

To drive well in the first place, you need to be in a positively stressed state, that is mentally and physically alert, to cope with the infinite variety of situations which occur at a split second's notice on the road. But stress in driving becomes harmful when it is aggravated by adverse conditions: heavy traffic and resulting congestion; the all too common aggression, bad manners and sloppy practice of other drivers; noise and vibration; mechanical problems with the car; diversions; tiredness – and even passengers! And other stress-related problems can make driving more stressful too: if your mind is preoccupied with these, your concentration and coordination, vital to good driving, will be impaired, and you will be more accident-prone.

Driver's keys to coping

Traffic jams: more than anything else on the road, hold-ups because of roadworks, accidents, or just sheer volume of traffic and inadequate roads to carry it, are calculated to send your blood pressure soaring. The element of frustration involved – you are literally powerless to do anything about getting caught in a traffic jam – is a powerful stressor, and this is compounded by many drivers' tendency to drive particularly selfishly in such situations – cutting in, moving unnecessarily from lane to lane, trying to jump the queue, and so on. Try not to be one of them. If you can see that the hold-up is likely to last some time, turn off the engine to keep the car cool, play one of your most soothing cassettes, or listen to the radio. And if you anticipate traffic jams – at a certain time on your way to work, for instance – do your best to avoid them, by leaving home a little earlier, for example.

Other drivers: it is often remarked that driving brings out the worst in people. Certainly it can make an aggressive type of person more so, and can also bring out a hostile side in people who are normally placid and controlled. If you find yourself subjected to discourteous or objectionable behaviour on the road, do your very best not to retaliate, by reminding yourself that confrontations on the road not only add to stress – they are highly dangerous and the cause of many accidents.

Mechanical problems: these are every motorist's bugbear, and powerful stressors. But there are plenty of practical steps you can take to avoid them: by making sure that your car is not only regularly serviced, but checked by you frequently, especially before a long journey, to make sure that the tyre-treads and pressure are all they should be, that you have sufficient oil as well as petrol, that your brakes, lights and steering are all in good working order. Learn to change a tyre yourself, and give yourself overall reassurance against stress by joining an organization such as the AA or RAC which can be called on in an emergency.

Tiredness: muscular contraction, the result of sitting in an incorrect posture, or of mental tension when feeling frustrated, irritated or impatient, causes considerable fatigue at the wheel. So it is important to make sure that you are really comfortable in the driving seat, particularly in the back, neck and shoulder areas. Use a special support cushion or head-rest if this is helpful, and make sure that you do not sit with hunched shoulders, and do not grip the wheel tightly. Relax your neck muscles by making small circling movements with your head while the car is temporarily at a halt – at traffic lights, for example – and practise some simple deep breathing too. Make sure that plenty of fresh air circulates through the car, either from the windows or ventilators.

Make it a rule not to drive for longer than three hours maximum without a break. If you start to feel tired, pull into a layby for a rest, a breath of air or a short walk to stretch your legs, or stop at a service station and have a coffee before resuming your journey. Fatigue makes you lose concentration and can easily cause accidents.

Passengers: passengers can inadvertently cause considerable stress to the driver of the vehicle in which they are travelling, and should be aware of a few do's and don'ts in this respect. 'Backseat drivers' are notoriously stressful passengers: they should be made to realize that the driver is in full, sole charge of the car, and they should not interfere or nag – this can be distracting as well as extremely annoying. On the other hand, a passenger can do a great deal to help the driver remain stress-free, by keeping a close eye on the road, and map-reading when necessary – getting lost, or taking the wrong turning, can be very stressful for the driver.

When children are passengers in the car, they must understand that they are on no account to distract the driver. They should ride in the back whenever possible, suitably restricted for safety purposes as described in rule 36 of the Highway Code, and on long journeys should be provided with plenty of games and projects which can be carried out safely in the car, to hold their attention and prevent them from becoming a nuisance.

Train travel

Overcrowded roads and the general aggravation the motorist all too often has to face, can make rail travel seem an attractive alternative to driving. The stressful burden of responsibility involved in getting from point A to point B by car is removed; and you can use the travelling time profitably to read, relax, or catch up on work in the train.

But travelling by train has stresses of its own too. Top of the list come cancellations and delays, which all commuters have to suffer at one time or another. Inadequate information or warnings about these, together with an absence of apology, can make these all the more frustrating and stressful.

Railway stations tend to be crowded, dirty and noisy places, and crowds, dirty, uncomfortable conditions, and high noise levels are all readily identifiable stressors. Long queues at ticket offices, and possible discourtesy from staff, are every bit as stressful as traffic jams and the bad behaviour of other road users to the motorist.

Commuter's keys to coping

Although you are inevitably in others' hands when you travel by rail, and not in a position to control the factors which cause stress, there are still a number of basic precautions you can take to keep the stress to a minimum.

■ If you travel regularly by train, buy a season ticket, and save yourself money as well as the stressful aggravation of waiting in queues. Many firms will help employees avail themselves of this facility by lending the money towards the purchase of a season ticket.

■ Stagger your travelling times if possible, to avoid rush hours. Flexi-time, practised successfully by many companies, is invaluable in this respect.

■ Make optimum use of your travelling time. Reading a good book or getting fully informed on some aspect of your work, for instance, will create a real sense of achievement, even if your journey has taken longer than expected, and will more than counterbalance any adverse stress caused.

■ If a group of you travels together regularly, you could all join in a shared activity, such as a game of bridge. Some commuters really get organized and arrange language learning or wine appreciation courses, lectures by guest speakers on various topics of common interest, for instance, to get the most out of their travelling time, and make the journey more enjoyable.

FIVE

BABY STRESS

Having a baby can and should be one of the most rewarding and fulfilling experiences for a woman; indeed many women, when asked to describe their immediate feelings on holding their newborn baby for the first time, say that it is as though the whole of their life suddenly seems to fall into place.

Pregnancy is one of the great life-changes, and as such can also be highly stressful, for wide-ranging reasons. It brings radical physical changes, as the mother's body system adapts to support the growing fetus, and these are accompanied by mood changes – often quite pronounced. On top of all this, there are likely to be feelings of apprehension – commonly associated with stress – especially in the case of a first baby; a mixture of very understandable anxiety about the actual labour and delivery, and an overall awareness that life will never be the same again. The realization that you will be totally responsible for the welfare of a brand-new human being 24 hours a day for many years to come can be quite overwhelming! And there may also be financial worries, which as already seen frequently cause stress: having a baby, especially if you have been used to working in a job which you are giving up, even temporarily, can seem a remarkably expensive business.

Body awareness

As with all forms of stress, understanding what causes it forms the ideal basis for coping. In order to appreciate the special stresses and strains of pregnancy, and come to terms with them, the very best start you can make is to familiarize yourself with the major changes that will take place in your body as it adapts to its new role of life support system for the baby. If, for example, you are aware that the volume of your blood will increase by a quite amazing 40 per cent to meet the demands of the growing fetus in terms of oxygen and nutrients extracted through the placenta, you will be in a strong position to appreciate the importance of a well-balanced diet in pregnancy, and to understand and cope with other physical and emotional changes. When you feel very tired, as many pregnant women do, or experience palpitations as the heart works overtime to pump the increased volume of blood around the system, understanding why you feel like this will do a lot to reduce the stressful aspect, and help you to cope.

Ante-natal care

A remarkable package of ante-natal care is available to pregnant women, and taking full advantage of it is one of the very best ways of minimizing stress in pregnancy.

It is very important to attend the ante-natal clinic at your health centre, hospital or GP unit, so as to benefit from the complete range of services offered by the team of professionals, including your GP, obstetrician, nursing staff, midwife and health visitor, who will be looking after you throughout your pregnancy. Awareness of the extent of this team effort can be particularly reassuring to new mothers, and do a lot to dispel stressful feelings.

During your pre-booked visits to the ante-natal clinic you will have the opportunity to get informed by asking questions, to seek any special reassurance you may require, and to get to know the various members of the medical team.

Most importantly from a stress point of view, you will benefit from very careful monitoring throughout your pregnancy. Sophisticated ante-natal screening devices, such as the detailed ultrasound scan which will give you your very first picture of your child, can provide immense reassurance to mothers-to-be.

Ante-natal classes

These are usually organized by your GP unit, health centre or hospital, or through the National Childbirth Trust on a local basis, and can do a lot to make the pregnancy a really enjoyable, stress-free experience for both mother and partner. The fact that your partner will be welcome at the classes not only helps him feel involved, but enables you both to share the experience and talk through any problems together in a mutually involved way. This joint participation is invaluable because it means that you will not have to experience the stress all too familiar to some pregnant women, when it seems that after the initial euphoric excitement of learning of the pregnancy, they are left to cope with it all on their own.

At the ante-natal classes you will be taught special exercises to help you cope with the physical stresses and strains of pregnancy. There will be special exercises for the pelvic floor and abdominal muscles, and others to ensure good circulation. You will also be taught deep breathing and relaxation techniques, both recognized methods of coping with stress, but in this instance specifically designed to help you during labour.

The ante-natal classes will also do much to alleviate stressful feelings of apprehension about labour, by explaining what signs to expect when it starts, and providing demonstrations of the different kinds of delivery, and comprehensive information on the various methods of pain relief that will be available to you.

Many new mothers find thinking about how they will cope with the baby when they first come home just as stressful as the anticipation of the birth itself, and again, the ante-natal classes will do a lot to help here. You will be shown how to handle a new baby, how to feed and bathe it, change nappies, and cope with all the other aspects of babycare. Useful advice will be given on what you need to buy for the baby, and what to take into hospital, so that you will feel fully prepared.

Arrangements are often made for the ante-natal class to visit the maternity ward to meet the staff, and find out in advance what the hospital procedures are – an invaluable process, as recognizing even one familiar face when you go into hospital can make a tremendous difference to the way you feel.

Most importantly, stress-wise, ante-natal classes offer the chance to meet others mums-to-be, to talk, and listen to other people's experiences. They also tend to be very cheery places, and it's nice to remember that laughter can be one of the most effective ways of dissipating stress! (See page 111.)

Rest and exercise during pregnancy

The extra demands made on the mother-to-be's energy reserves are compensated for naturally by a general slowing-down of the body functions, resulting in the placidity often associated with pregnancy in the later stages. But you can also make your own contribution to reducing the kind of stress associated with physical tiredness during pregnancy by maintaining your energy levels and making sure you get plenty of rest. Help your body now that it has embarked upon the strenuous course of supporting two lives instead of one by making a point of putting your feet up and practising some simple relaxation techniques even at short intervals during the course of the day.

At the same time, you need to keep up some regular form of exercise, to ensure that your circulation continues to work well, and your joints remain supple. Swimming is one of the most highly recommended forms of exercise during pregnancy, as it is so relaxing, and can be continued safely into the late stages.

The pregnant diet

Following a sensibly varied and well-balanced diet is one of the many practical ways of coping with stress generally, and there is more about this in chapter 8. Diet is especially important during pregnancy, when eating the right foods can do a great deal to ensure that the developing fetus is getting the right nourishment, and that the extra drain on the mother's resources is being adequately compensated.

It may sound obvious, but eating properly really is a highly effective way of keeping harmful stress at bay. The following foods are specially important during pregnancy and should be included regularly in the diet:

□ *lean meat and fish*, for body-building protein
□ *cheese, yogurt and milk*, to ensure good supplies of calcium
□ *liver*, a valuable source for the extra intake of iron recommended for pregnant women to counter any tendency towards anaemia
□ *fresh fruit and vegetables*, especially leafy green vegetables
□ *high-fibre foods*, such as pulses, to help keep the system

regular and avoid the constipation to which pregnant women are prone

□ *potatoes and wholegrain bread*, important sources of complex carbohydrate, for energy, as opposed to the refined carbohydrate of sugar and sweets, which should be cut down

Know your rights

As already mentioned, on a purely practical level having a baby can work out quite a lot more expensive than you might expect. Making sure that you are fully informed about all that you are entitled to from the social services during and after pregnancy is one very positive way of pre-empting possible stress from the extra drain on financial resources which a new baby inevitably represents. Adapting to this will seem much easier if you take steps to find out about:

□ maternity leave benefits
□ child allowance benefits
□ free NHS prescriptions during pregnancy
□ free dental care during pregnancy and for 1 year following the birth

AIMS and Maternity Alliance (see chapter 10) are excellent sources of such information.

Getting organized

A lot of potential stress around the time of the actual birth can be reduced by planning ahead as far as possible. If you have worked previously, it's always tempting to stay on in your job just a little too long, but it is much more sensible in the long run, for your own peace of mind as well as the baby's well-being, if you do not cut things too fine.

Give yourself plenty of time to get everything you need ready for the baby – particularly, of course, if it is a first baby. You may want to adapt and decorate a room in the house specially for nursery use – don't leave this too late. As there's always the possibility that the baby may come early, don't be taken by surprise, and have everything necessary for the arrival ready a month before. (Mothercare sells a layette containing everything required for looking after a new baby, down to the very smallest items, and this would take a lot of hassle out of shopping for the essentials. Mothercare's mail order facilities are also invaluable.) Make sure, too, that everything you will need for yourself in hospital is ready and packed well in advance, to avoid last-minute panics.

A stress-free birth

Every woman is likely to have her own preferences about the way she would like to deliver her baby; there is a wide range of choice, and fortunately more and more hospitals are able and willing to cooperate with individual wishes.

You may wish to have a 'natural' birth, relying on the labour positions and deep breathing techniques you have been taught. You may have investigated the possibilities of pain relief offered by acupuncture or transcutaneous nerve stimulation, or you may prefer to accept some of the more conventional methods available in labour, such as pethidine (pain-killer by injection), epidural anaesthetic (insertion of tube into spinal cord), or entonox, often called 'gas and oxygen' (a mixture of nitrous oxide and oxygen inhaled through a mask). Whatever decision you may have made in advance, it is a good idea to keep an open mind and remain flexible. You can do a great deal to minimize the stress of labour by developing a good two-way relationship with the midwife, and the presence of your husband or partner, or perhaps of your mother, sister or a close friend, can also be very reassuring and helpful.

Home birth

Giving birth in the familiar surroundings of your own home means that you will not have to cope with the stress of adapting to the inevitably clinical atmosphere of a hospital ward. A home birth may be something you want to think about seriously, but you must be guided by your doctor on this. If it is felt that for any reason you would be better off in hospital, with easy access to specialist equipment, for example, you should respect this view.

Breast- or bottle-feeding

Breast-feeding can have its stressful side while you and the baby are learning the techniques, but once these have been mastered, it can be a uniquely close and soothing experience, in marked contrast in its natural simplicity with the paraphernalia of bottle-feeding. However, bottle-feeding has its advantages too, and you should not allow yourself to get stressed or upset if for any reason you are unable to breast-feed your baby: again, a flexible outlook is your best course.

Bonding

Breast-feeding contributes very importantly to the bonding process which is now widely acknowledged to play such an important part in human development. Certainly, the importance of bonding can be appreciated when the act of birth is considered from the baby's point of view. Leaving the warmth, darkness and silence of the womb, and at the same time immediately transferring from one system of breathing to another, makes birth the greatest of all the life-changes, and as such highly stressful in itself.

Immediate bonding between mother and child can do much to reduce the 'distress' of birth: if the mother can hold the baby close to her immediately it is born, this will do much to provide the best possible start to life with minimum stress.

At home

If your baby has been delivered in hospital, your natural longing to get it home may be diluted by equally natural feelings of apprehension. You will probably experience some of the kind of stress that occurs when you drive a car on your own for the first time after passing your driving test. You will of course be able to draw on the practical knowledge gained during your ante-natal classes, but anxiety about caring for the new baby for real will be considerably allayed as well by being aware of the supportive post-natal care that will be available to you.

Your midwife will call at least once a day for 3 weeks, to check on the baby's well-being and your recovery. After she stops coming she will be replaced by a health visitor, who may also be able to arrange for a home help. If you have a toddler, she may be able to arrange for him or her to be looked after in a day nursery, to give you more time to get to know the new baby.

If you can afford it, you may wish to arrange for a temporary nanny to live in for the first few weeks after bringing a new baby home. This is especially helpful if the nanny has come through a strong personal recommendation, but do bear in mind that the presence of a stranger, however professional and well-meaning, after such a major upheaval as giving birth may seem like yet another form of disruption to the routine to cope with. Many new mothers would probably ideally prefer their own mother to come to stay for a short time, if feasible.

Whatever the source, don't be proud about accepting all the help you can get, to ease adjustment to your new life with the baby. You will need to catch up on as much sleep as you can yourself, especially as nights will have to be broken for feeding purposes, even if the baby is otherwise a sound sleeper.

Baby blues

This is the term commonly used to describe post-partum depression, a common condition of physical origin manifesting itself emotionally, and linked to hormonal changes as the body reverts to its pre-pregnant state. Fortunately it is usually of short duration, but it can raise stress levels if it persists, so if you are worried, do consult your doctor, who will be able to advise.

Losing a baby

The loss of a baby through still birth or a cot death is an overwhelming event to come to terms with. Your own feelings of grief and shock, isolation, frustration, guilt and anger may result in emotional confusion, compounded by the fact that even close friends and family may find it impossible to speak to you to convey their sympathy fully over something so devastating. This kind of taboo all too often compounds the highly stressful feelings of unfounded guilt which many parents bereaved in this way experience.

Professional counselling, with sensitive suggestions of ways to cope, and guidance on how to handle the grieving process from people who have shared the same experience, may be the best course. Self-help support groups, in particular SANDS (Stillbirth and Neonatal Death Society), details of which may be found in chapter 10, offer invaluable help in this direction.

SIX

CHILDREN UNDER STRESS

Stress is by no means an exclusively adult problem. Children can suffer from the effects of harmful stress every bit as much. In fact, stress is all the more difficult for children to handle because they are not yet in a position to think it through and isolate its sources to see how these affect them personally, in the way that adults can.

Because children cannot be expected to help themselves in the same way as adults, they need and deserve plenty of guidance in stress management. Children from broken or unstable homes are more obvious candidates for stress-related problems, but all children will experience stress in some form, more or less, as part of growing up. As seen in chapter 5, the transition from the security of the womb to the challenge of the world outside is the greatest – and perhaps most stressful – of all the life-changes we share. The subsequent years of childhood, especially the years up to the age of 5, continue to be a time of enormous changes, which often follow each other in rapid succession.

This is when a child learns to walk, to talk, to feed him or herself, to relate to others within the close circle of the family and the wider context of school, to distinguish right from wrong, to assess possible sources of danger, and take the right action accordingly. It is a time of almost constant adjustment to new situations and given that stress is so closely linked to various forms of change, it is easy to appreciate just how stressful life may seem to young children. Classic childhood stress symptoms may include a tendency to stammer, which most usually develops around the age of 4–5, when fluent speech is normally achieved, or a tendency to tell lies.

Such manifestations of stress are usually quite easily dealt with, and short-lived, but they all require prompt attention. Children have to be taught to cope with stress from an early age: if this can be achieved successfully, it will provide them with a sound foundation for handling more complex forms of stress later in life. It is therefore very important for adults to be able to identify the sort of situations which may cause individual children difficulties – these may be as various as a fear of the dark, or of being left alone, learning how to share things, or how to take teasing.

Given that children have everything to learn as they embark upon their lives, it is not surprising that they frequently experience feelings of uncertainty, and as we have seen, uncertainty and stress often go in tandem. Children need firm and fair direction to overcome these uncertainties, and encouragement to help them to learn to make their own decisions as a first step towards coping successfully with stress.

Parent–child relations

A child's best protection against everyday stresses and strains is to be able to count on love and security in the immediate surroundings of home. But relations between children and their parents, being a series of ongoing mutual adjustments and adaptation, can themselves be fraught with stress, on both sides. In particular, parents who have themselves experienced unstable childhoods or broken homes may find it difficult to adapt to becoming parents themselves. Or, for one reason or another, parents may not be able to spend as much time with their children as desirable. Antagonism may arise if a parent does not particularly like one of the children, or has a marked preference for one child above the others. Such a situation is not uncommon, and certainly the stress of it can be greatly relieved if parents are prepared to face up to the fact, and perhaps consider some professional help in this respect: some useful contact organizations, for example Exploring Parenthood, are given in chapter 10.

Sibling relations

A child's relations with brothers and sisters are often his or her first taste of belonging to a peer group, with all that this involves in the way of both companionship and competition. Depending on a variety of factors, in particular age differences and position in the sibling hierarchy, children usually experience some form of rivalry and conflict with brothers and sisters, often depending on whether they are the eldest/youngest/in the middle, and so on. It is important for parents to remain alert to stressful problems that may arise in this area, and deal with them effectively early on, though sibling-related stress can continue to manifest later in life too: for example, when a brother or sister leaves home, gets engaged or married.

One of the earliest manifestations of stress between siblings often occurs with the arrival of a new baby in the family. The birth of a new brother or sister can result in quite painful feelings of displacement in an older child, which can in turn cause considerable stress, often expressing itself in the form of acute jealousy and resentment. Recognition of this by parents can go a long way towards solving it, and there are many practical ways in which they can prepare a child for the arrival of a new baby, and minimize the stress of the situation as a result.

For example, it is a good idea to explain the new arrival well in advance, involving the older child by making it clear that his or her help will be invaluable when the time comes, and greatly appreciated. And when the new baby is actually brought home for the first time, it is extremely important to reassure the older child, letting him know that he continues to be loved as much as ever, even if he is no longer the centre of attention. This is a vital stage in the learning-to-share process, which is crucial to all children's development.

Stress at school

Going to school is a major step for all children. It is at school that they usually find themselves within a peer group proper for the first time, and inevitably, learning to cope and adapt, as they will later as adults in a broader society, creates stress. School brings children face to face with the competitiveness which they will experience at all stages in their working lives; one of the major childhood stressors is the way children are exposed to competitive stress earlier and earlier. For example, attending a nursery group is one of the recognized ways of minimizing the stress of going to 'proper' school at the age of 5, as required by law, but places in good nursery groups and play schools are always in too short supply for the demand, and even these places have to be competed for.

Some of the special stresses children commonly encounter at school include:

☐ problems with work: all children now have to achieve a certain level of computer-literacy, which can cause special difficulties

☐ making friends: learning how to establish friendships, how to be popular and 'one of the crowd', or how to cope with losing a 'best friend'

☐ bullying

☐ disliking or being disliked by a particular teacher

☐ having fewer material possessions, or less pocket money than school friends

☐ taking exams

☐ changes in school: not just from kindergarten to infants, primary to secondary, but perhaps from one area to another, with accompanying loss of friends and changes in the curriculum

☐ being a gifted child, which can create the special stresses associated with being the 'odd man out', excluded from the main crowd

☐ unreasonable parental expectations

☐ the disruption of teacher shortages and strikes

Keys to reducing stress at school

Fortunately there is a great deal parents can do to help their children cope with all these forms of stress at school. Understanding and support at home are invaluable, and can be expressed in a variety of constructive ways.

■ When setting up home or thinking of moving house, bear in mind the local schools in the area you are considering: for many parents, the school they feel is right for their children will be a strong factor in deciding where to live.

- Avoid the temptation of pressing your child too hard to achieve results. Awareness of high parental expectations can be a spur, but if overdone can be stressful.

- Much better than pressurizing and nagging is to show a genuine, sustained interest in school work and activities.

- Be sure to ask your child about his or her day at school, and take time to listen to what he has to say.

- All you can do for your child at pre-school age in the way of encouraging reading, writing and other basic skills, will be of inestimable help later on, reflected not just in the classroom, but in your child's whole attitude towards learning as something to be enjoyed.

- Within reason, make sure that friends from school are welcomed into your home. It's one of the best ways available to you for seeing who your child is spending time with, as well as helping in the development of social skills.

- Get involved yourself in the life of your child's school: join in school activities, such as drama and fund-raising.

- Attend parent-teacher meetings regularly. In this way you will not only get direct feedback on how your child is doing, but will yourself be positively demonstrating your interest. Under the 1989 Education Act, teachers are now contractually obliged to work more closely with parents. By getting to know your child's teachers, you will also be able to appreciate for yourself the special stresses to which they are prone, by the nature of their profession.

- Encourage joint family activities out of school in which everyone can take part enjoyably, such as visits to the zoo, museums, or nature trails.

- If your child shows a special interest and ability, such as in a sport, in playing a musical instrument, or chess, for example, do everything you can to encourage and support it. Extra-curricular activities are an important counterpart to school itself, and can help achieve the kind of balance which is what stress-free living is all about.

■ School makes considerable demands on children, and it is when they cannot respond adequately or satisfactorily to these demands that it becomes stressful. Truancy, or feigned illness, are classic symptoms of stress in schoolchildren, so keep a watchful eye open for these, and take appropriate action early on.

Stress and illness

Illness at any stage is a powerful stressor, for both invalid and carer, but can be especially so during childhood. Any break from familiar routine, which illness represents, can cause stress, and it is sometimes difficult to explain to children why they are feeling unwell, or what the nature of the pain they are experiencing is.

Childhood illness can be even more stressful for parents, too. In the case of minor illness, it is not always easy to know when and if the doctor should be called: children are remarkably resilient and may recover very quickly, and some doctors have a tendency to label mothers as neurotic if they show signs of over-anxiety for their children's state of health.

In the case of serious illness requiring hospitalization, stress is often caused by the unfamiliar surroundings of the hospital itself, although fortunately in children's hospitals every effort is made to create a cheerful and relaxed, as well as caring, environment, to put the patients at their ease as far as possible. Many children's hospitals can offer parents overnight accommodation so that they do not have to leave their children, which can be a tremendous boon in helping to keep the stress down on both sides. The National Association for the Welfare of Children in Hospital does sterling work in this respect: details in chapter 10.

The stress of illness can nevertheless affect all the family; it may be difficult for other children not to be, or at any rate to feel, neglected while their parents are preoccupied – this also applies in the case of handicapped children who may require a lot of extra attention. It can be a real challenge to parents in these circumstances to find ways of compensating for this.

The stress of adolescence

Adolescence can be a highly stressful time for all the family, as anyone who has coped with teenage mood-changes will know all too well. To understand and sympathize with the special stresses and strains of adolescence, it is helpful to consider these in the context of the powerful changes, physical and emotional, which characterize this 'awkward' life stage.

Adolescents have to cope with all the body changes of puberty, which can be overwhelming, and at the same time with their changing attitudes towards the opposite sex; orientation in this respect can be a complicated and often painful process. They will also undergo deep changes in their attitudes to the family, which may range from point-blank refusal to go on the usual family annual holiday, to total rejection of parental authority and values as they learn to distance themselves from the family's protective environment. This is also a time when attitudes to school and peer groups may change quite drastically, as part of teenagers' new awareness of themselves in relation to society and the law.

It can be especially difficult to help children cope with stress at this time because rejection of such help is itself part and parcel of the growing-up process. Endless patience and tact as well as a strong sense of humour are required; it may help to recall frequently that this period of experimentation with whole sets of new values is temporary, but a crucial transition period in the process of becoming a well-balanced human being.

It is sometimes worth bearing in mind that adolescents may prefer to talk over any specific or more general problems they may have with another relative or close family friend, or the parents of a school friend, rather than their own parents.

Children of divorce

Given that stress is closely linked to change and often intensified by uncertainty, it is easy to appreciate why the children of divorced or divorcing parents often experience stress to an equally great, if not greater, degree as their parents. Depending on the circumstances of the divorce, the parents are likely to be preoccupied with major practical changes in living arrangements, finances, contact with children, all accompanied by feelings of vulnerability, lowered self-esteem, depression, emotional exhaustion, role-uncertainty, loneliness and loss of sense of purpose and motivation. Many of these emotions will undoubtedly affect the children involved, who may of course have had previous unhappy experiences of overhearing rows, witnessing angry scenes, and so on.

Keys to helping children cope with divorce

Children are often rightly described as the innocent victims of divorce. There is much that parents can do to help their children cope with a situation that is not of their making, but unfortunately, at such an emotionally charged time, they may often not be feeling in the right frame of mind to discuss the situation as fully, frankly and objectively as they would wish. The children's age is obviously an important factor, but the following basic pointers are useful working guidelines.

■ Make sure that your children realize that they are in no way responsible for what has happened to their parents. This is such an obvious point that it can tend to be overlooked sometimes, with the result that children may build up stress based on guilt, silently feeling that they must be in some way to blame if their parents do not want to live together any more.

■ Avoid making hostile remarks about your partner, as these will confuse children further.

■ Be as specific as you can about access arrangements, once these are finalized, so that the children know exactly where they stand.

■ To minimize stressful uncertainty, make sure that all arrangements for collecting children, taking them out, or having them to stay, are strictly adhered to.

■ The National Family Conciliation Council (see chapter 10) exists to help divorcing and separated couples resolve problems and conflicts, especially those concerning their children, and it is well worth bearing this and other such organizations in mind if you run into difficulties.

Step-family stress

The fact that one-third of marriages end in divorce does not prevent remarriage from becoming increasingly popular, most often with one or both parents bringing children from previous marriages. This means that a large number of children are living in a remarriage set-up, and consequently the step-family situation is becoming increasingly the norm.

Adjusting to a new step-parent and step-siblings can be a notoriously stressful process, and developing a sound and valuable relationship one of the most difficult achievements for both step-parent and step-child. Not infrequently, problems with step-children can result in unforeseen stress between couples, which may be deliberately or unconsciously cultivated by the children if they continue to be unhappy themselves. On the other hand, children are often quick to see that they may be able to enjoy the best of two worlds in the step-situation. They will also most likely have friends at school in a similar situation, with whom they can exchange impressions, and thus feel they are not alone.

The step-parent's keys to adjusting
Establishing successful, stress-free relations within a step-family unit is undoubtedly a major challenge, but the rewards can be very great. If you find yourself in a new role of step-parent, you may find it useful to remember the following points.

■ Go easy to start with; don't expect too much too soon; remember that you need to win the children's confidence.

■ It may be best, depending on the age of the children, not to attempt to replace a lost or displaced parent, but rather make it clear that you would prefer to be regarded as a close and trusted friend.

■ There are bound to be times when the situation will try your patience – for example, if you have to put up with long-term hostility or cold-shouldering – but do all you can to be sensitive and try to see the situation through the eyes of a child whose world has been turned topsy-turvy.

■ Try as far as possible to remain detached in relation to the children's natural mother or father, whom they may have lost through bereavement or divorce. In neither case is it wise to ignore the existence of the absent parent, or to make him or her the object of criticism or hostility.

- Try in all cases to talk openly, to avoid the impression of hiding things from the children.

- In your efforts to adjust to your new family, be fair in relation to your own children; avoid double standards, and try not to favour them, or conversely, to let them feel left out; aim for the best possible relations between them and their new step-brothers and sisters, but remember that this is all bound to take time, so try not to be impatient.

- If you have a child of your own after taking over the role of step-mother or step-father to your partner's children, be careful not to seem to lose interest in them while you are absorbed in your own new baby, by remaining aware of how unfair this would be on children whose confidence you have won.

- The National Stepfamily Association (details in chapter 10) offers a comprehensive counselling service to help all members of step-families meet the special challenges facing them.

Child abuse

As discussed in chapter 5, bonding with the mother is widely regarded as the best possible start in life for a new baby, but it is a sad fact that 5–10 per cent of mothers do not take naturally to the maternal process, with stressful consequences for both themselves and their children. Battered babies and children subjected to various kinds of abuse are all too often the victims of parents who suffer from inability to adapt to their parental role because of stress problems experienced in their own childhoods – a vicious circle if ever there was one. Abused children probably suffer from the most extreme forms of stress that an unhappy childhood has to offer, often compounded by feelings of unfounded guilt.

In recent years a great deal of publicity has highlighted the plight of such children, particularly those who have suffered from some form of sexual abuse by a parent or other family member. Hopefully, this attention will in itself achieve reduction in the painful stress levels such treatment makes children endure, by creating a much greater awareness of their problems on the part of both the public and professional caring bodies. Details of some of the latter, such as Childline, can be found in chapter 10.

SEVEN

STRESS IN OLD AGE

Two of the most powerful of all stressors, change and uncertainty, particularly affect elderly people, of whom Britain has an estimated population of three million – many of them, thanks to improved healthcare, better living standards and increased longevity, reaching the age of 85 and beyond. Stress is widely recognized as a problem many old people have to contend with, and its treatment is accordingly regarded as an integral part of caring for the aged.

Two kinds of change in particular can adversely affect, even overwhelm, old people: changes in their own situation, which may seem unfamiliar and beyond their control; and changes in the world about them which may seem frightening or threatening because they do not understand them and are consequently not in a position to come to terms with them.

A classic example of the first type of change is what happens when old people find themselves in the position of living alone and unable to look after themselves; and of the second, the very real state of fear in which many old people live as a result of our increasingly violent society. On a less drastic level, even everyday facts of modern living, such as the increased volume of traffic, or the proliferation of bureaucratic red tape, can cause old people stress, as in instances when they experience problems with crossing busy roads, or filling in complicated forms.

Isolation and loneliness are two of the special stress-related problems many old people face – in inner cities as well as in remote rural areas. The supportive extended family unit is no longer a social norm in this country, and old people inevitably often suffer as a result. They may find themselves living far away from their families, or have no contact with family at all. Yet perhaps just as bad can be sharing a home with a son or daughter in a stressful atmosphere, which can all too easily arise if such an arrangement has not been properly planned and thought through.

Bereavement, always a highly stressful experience, can be devastating for old people. The death of a spouse rates as the most severe stressor of all (see the stress rating scale on page 46), and is obviously extra-hard to cope with when it marks the end of a long-standing loving relationship and a companionship of many years. Bereavement can create acute isolation problems, especially for women, who tend to be longer-lived than men, which may be compounded by money worries if the surviving partner is left not knowing how to cope, or if financial arrangements, such as a pension or fixed income, do not keep abreast of inflation. Losing a partner may also leave widows and widowers contemplating the great unknown of their own death, itself a powerful source of fear-related stress, especially in our society where death remains a taboo subject which the majority of people find they cannot talk about – although talking might help a great deal in releasing stress. This is where organizations like CRUSE, which specializes in bereavement care and counselling (details in chapter 10), can often be of tremendous assistance and comfort.

In fact, fewer opportunities to talk and be listened to is frequently in itself another cause of stress in old age. Remembering the past means a great deal to many old people – reminiscence is sometimes used in group therapy for the elderly, who are encouraged to recount and discuss their memories – and the sheer documentary value of these recollections is of immense interest and value. Younger people can do a lot to help the elderly cope with stress by being good listeners and taking some time out from their busy lives to become so. Certainly, talking and being listened to does a great deal to alleviate the loss of self-esteem and feelings of uselessness and worthlessness, which many old people experience in reaction to society's cult of youth.

Keys to coping with retirement

It seems sad and wrong that old people nearing the end of their lives should have to continue to cope with problems of stress, but fortunately there are some excellent organizations for all aspects of the care of the elderly, details of which can be found in chapter 10. And there is a great deal of positive action which old people can consider taking to help themselves lead a less stressed existence as well. Here are some examples.

■ Look ahead to retirement, which should be something to anticipate with pleasure, but can turn out to be an unexpectedly stressful time if you are not prepared for it – the boredom of empty days, for example, can be stressful, as can even the unfamiliar situation of spending 24 hours a day in the company of a spouse. So plan your retirement in advance as far as possible, taking practical precautions with insurance schemes, and giving plenty of thought to where you will live: ideally you should not need to think about moving again after retirement.

■ The Pre-Retirement Association of Great Britain and Northern Ireland (details in chapter 10) offers useful advice on planning retirement and getting the most out of it when it comes.

■ Make sure your affairs are in order, for your own peace of mind as well as for the welfare of others. There is nothing morbid about looking ahead in this way; knowing that you have made all the proper arrangements, like drawing up a will, leaves you free to enjoy life fully in the present without worrying about the future.

■ Take the opportunity in retirement of making sure that you know how to do a variety of household tasks, so as to be in a position to look after yourself should the necessity arise. Cooking classes, for example, can be great fun when you are retired and have more time available, as well as teaching a very useful, practical skill.

■ Keep up with old friends and do all you can to make new ones – don't rely too heavily on your immediate family.

■ Develop a relationship with your grandchildren – this can often be very special and rewarding – but don't take on more than you can cope with easily. For example, you may find having young grandchildren to stay surprisingly tiring and stressful, and visits of this kind are probably best kept brief.

- Keep physically active: as much physical exercise as you can comfortably and enjoyably manage will help reduce stress and maintain good circulation, especially important in old age.

- Keep mentally active too: make good use of your local adult education centre and of your local library facilities.

- Many pensioners take a part-time job, not only to help their budgets, but also to create an extra interest which can do a great deal to prevent stress. A job is also of course an excellent way of maintaining useful contact with people.

- You might also like to consider doing some voluntary work, perhaps for your local hospital or other locally based organizations: a comprehensive list of such organizations is available from the National Council for Voluntary Organizations (details in chapter 10). There is no better way of taking your mind off stresses of your own than doing something to help others.

- Keep socially active and get out as much as possible, to avoid unnecessary stress building up if you are alone at home: local societies, such as lunch clubs, the WI, bowling clubs and so on, have a great deal to offer, and many such organizations can arrange transport facilities. Even a simple meal at home can be an enjoyable social event if you invite a friend to share it with you.

- Make sure you eat properly. Keeping your energy reserves high by means of a good balanced diet is an important element in resisting harmful stress. Many people find they feel less hungry as they get older, but even if you eat less, your diet should be as varied as possible, so make this a priority.

- Sharing a home can often seem a welcome alternative to living alone, but usually requires a considerable process of adjustment. To make this as smooth and stress-free as possible, plenty of planning and forethought are necessary. Many families find a 'Granny flat' an ideal arrangement, as it offers more scope for independence than actually sharing the same living space; but either way it is extremely important for some basic 'house rules' to be laid down from the beginning, to ensure that everybody's expectations of the arrangement are the same.

Diet Tips for Older People

■ **Vary your diet**, for interest as well as nutritional value.

■ **Plan a week's meals in advance** (this makes shopping easier too), making sure that you are getting plenty of fresh fruit and vegetables, for roughage, some high-fibre foods like pulses and wholemeal bread, to avoid constipation, and sufficient protein (lean meat, chicken and fish are good sources).

■ **Make lunch your main meal of the day**: this is better for your digestive system than eating at night, and you are more likely to enjoy preparing, as well as eating, a meal in the middle of the day when you will be less tired.

■ **Cut down on high-fat, sugary and salty foods**, to keep your cholesterol levels low and reduce the risk of heart disease.

■ **Make sure your fluid intake is adequate**: even if you do not feel particularly thirsty, you must make sure you do not become dehydrated. Six–eight cups of fluid per day is about right, though it is best to avoid drinking fluids in the evening.

■ **Make sensible use of convenience foods**, such as ready-made meals, but don't overdo them: dishes made yourself from fresh ingredients are, of course, always preferable to preserved foods.

■ **Keep a store cupboard well-stocked with emergency rations**, in case you need to stay indoors for a while. Useful standbys might include:
- □ Sardines in tomato sauce
- □ Canned or packet soup
- □ Tuna in brine
- □ Dried pasta

Continued

Diet Tips – *continued*

- ☐ Baked beans and other ready-cooked canned pulses
- ☐ Can of new potatoes
- ☐ Can of peeled tomatoes
- ☐ Canned fruit in natural juice
- ☐ Canned creamed rice pudding
- ☐ Biscuits
- ☐ Crispbreads
- ☐ Peanut butter
- ☐ Marmalade

■ **Make good use of a home freezer**, if you have one, but be sure to label all items in the freezer clearly, and check the dates carefully from time to time. Discard any foods that have passed the use-by date – they can be a health hazard. In the same way, always check sell-by dates in shops, and ask if in doubt.

■ **Make good use of labour-saving devices in cooking**: food wrapped in a foil parcel cooks quickly and easily, as heat is distributed evenly and all the natural flavour and juices are retained; and there are no dishes or pans to wash up. The microwave oven is ideal in many ways for older people to use – in fact a microwave would make an ideal retirement present. It is super-quick and economical on fuel; all it needs is a regular wipe to keep it clean; it does away with the need for awkward saucepans, and makes excellent porridge, and scrambled eggs, as well as cooking fresh fish and vegetables to perfection.

It is also worth bearing in mind that British Gas offers a very useful service to older customers, which involves advising on choice and use of appliances, and even adapting controls on existing ones, for easier use. You can find details in the booklet *Advice for Senior Citizens*, available from British Gas showrooms.

■ Similarly, if you are considering living in sheltered accommodation, which is being built increasingly to meet old people's special requirements, it is important to market-research the idea thoroughly before coming to a decision. If you are looking at a property of this kind through an estate agent, bear in mind that property dealers often deliberately try to pressure people into buying, and older people can be particularly vulnerable in this respect. So don't let yourself get stressed in this way: allow yourself plenty of time, so that you won't need to come to a conclusion in a hurry, and can find out all you want to know; for example, what provision is made for service charges (these can rise quite alarmingly in some cases, so you need to be prepared), and whether your furniture will fit in (the rooms may well be quite a lot smaller than you are used to).

■ Keep vigilant: a particularly unpleasant and stressful threat has been posed to old people living alone in recent years, by thieves posing as doorstep salesman. Help the Aged ran a very successful campaign on this, fully supported by the government and the police. The campaign took a very positive view of ways to help the elderly to improve their home security. Advice included:
   □ Have a safety chain and viewing device installed on a front door.
   □ Never open the door if you feel uncertain, and always do so with the safety chain attached.
   □ Always ask for identity checks.
   □ If you are uncertain, ask the caller to return at a time when you can have a friend or relative with you.

■ Pets: a dog can also be very useful as a help with security – a bark is an excellent deterrent to intruders! Pets generally can do much to relieve stress in elderly people. The right pet can provide wonderful companionship, and caring for it creates a very special bond. The very act of stroking an affectionate, well-loved animal can be of immense therapeutic value: sitting quietly with a purring cat in your lap can be a tremendously reassuring and relaxing experience, a delightful way to keep stress levels low.

As you get older it is important to choose pets sensibly: for example, a boisterous dog requiring a great deal of exercise, such as a border collie, would not be as wise a choice, perhaps, as a King Charles spaniel. Many old people find a cat an ideal pet: it will not need to be exercised and can lead a quite independent sort of life, especially if you are able to have a cat flap on your door.

The time of your life

Help the Aged, one of a number of caring organizations for the elderly, full details of which can be found in chapter 10, has done tremendous work not just in terms of fund-raising to provide better facilities for old people, but as a valued information service on a wide range of topics, from advice on winter warmth, to filling in forms.

As well as numerous leaflets offering practical advice on different individual subjects to do with old age, Help the Aged publishes a very useful book, entitled *The Time of Your Life*, which comprehensively covers the full range of topics which can cause stress in the elderly. It may be ordered from Help the Aged (address on page 121) and is very well worth reading as a source of inspiration as well as reassurance. In it you will find information on such points as housing options in retirement; the pros and cons of moving; practical financial advice on budgeting, pensions, tax, entitlements, investments and making a will; a complete section on health, with advice on diet, keeping fit and involved, and the importance of regular medical checkups. There are also interesting personal accounts of how real-life pensioners have adjusted to retirement, providing an invaluable source of the kind of sympathetic information which can do so much to help relieve potentially damaging stress in old age.

Caring for the elderly

Caring for an elderly relative can create special stresses in terms of the demands it makes on the carer. Local social services are there to help, with meals on wheels and home helps, and the National Association of Carers (see chapter 10) offers invaluable supportive advice and counselling. In addition, the hospice movement, whose work is receiving ever-increasing acknowledgment and encouragement, can do much to assist carers, as well as those for whom they care, during the final phase.

EIGHT

STATE OF BODY
Stress Remedies

Current widespread awareness of the toll that excess, unreleased stress takes on both body and mind has resulted in increased interest in tackling it on an everyday basis by developing a happier, healthier, less stressed lifestyle; exercise, relaxation and a well-balanced diet are essential elements in this approach. Specific remedies which you can develop for yourself are suggested here and in the following chapter.

A very positive result of increasing stress-awareness is that the medical profession takes stress seriously; extensive research continues to be conducted into the causes and effects of stress, and how it can best be controlled. Physical illness and pain have long been recognized as active stressors, but it is now believed that mental stress can equally result in a general lowering of the body's immune system: for example, if you suffer from repeated colds that you just can't seem to shake off, it may well be that you are suffering from some form of stress.

Many doctors now regard encouraging their patients to relax, and advising them on ways in which they can best do so, as a welcome and effective means of reducing the use of prescribed tranquillizers and sedative drugs, which can of course become addictive. In fact the body is capable of manufacturing its own natural pain-killers and tranquillizers, and research is currently looking at the function of endorphins produced in the brain and how they can be stimulated through exercise to provide natural pain relief.

Certain common body disorders are considered to be specifically stress-related; of these, some are thought to be aggravated and perpetuated by stress, or may even develop as a direct result of it. These include skin and respiratory disorders, such as various allergies, eczema, psoriasis and asthma. Medical evidence shows that acute stress can also be particularly associated with hypertension (raised blood pressure), which if unmonitored and allowed to become severe or prolonged can result in narrowing and hardening of the arteries, a common cause of heart attacks and strokes. Preventive measures in terms of diet, relaxation and the right kind of exercise are recommended by doctors and may complement other prescribed treatment.

In some other disorders, particularly rheumatoid arthritis, it is felt that there may well be a link with stress, but this is difficult to prove conclusively.

Stress often plays a part in the development of ulcers, particularly in people who put themselves under stress by overworking for long periods, especially on an empty stomach. Ulcers occur when the secretion of gastric acid in the stomach is increased, with a corresponding decrease in the secretion of the protective mucus coating, so that the acid damages the stomach lining through this breakdown in the body's defence mechanism. Smoking and alcohol – especially when alcohol is drunk without accompanying food – aggravate ulcers, and doctors also advise against eating fried fatty or spicy foods.

Headaches are very often stress-related, caused by mental pressure leading to muscular contraction which constricts the blood vessels. Insomnia, too, is a common symptom of stress. Apart from chronic sufferers, most people have had some experience of inability to sleep when the mind seems to refuse to shut down for the night and goes on working overtime. Length and depth of sleep required are individual matters, but the natural recuperative process of sound, restful sleep is essential to restore and refresh the body, and regular rhythms and patterns of sleep are themselves beneficial in resisting stress.

Keys to coping with insomnia

- Take some form of physical exercise during the day.

- Be sure to get as much fresh air as possible during the day.

- Avoid a heavy evening meal.

- Avoid excess alcohol and caffeine at night.

- Don't go to bed until you feel sleepy.

- Don't take work to bed with you.

- Read a few pages of an untaxing book shortly before you want to go to sleep.

- Make yourself a soothing bedtime drink.

- If you often find yourself lying awake, consider learning the autogenic relaxation techniques outlined on pages 106–7.

- Make sure your bed is really comfortable: top quality beds come very expensive, but this is one piece of furniture that is well worth a substantial investment.

When stress lies behind insomnia, it is infinitely preferable to locate and deal with its cause, rather than to resort to sleeping pills, which can only provide temporary relief and can easily become addictive. If you have been experiencing particularly stressful problems in your life which prevent you from sleeping, your doctor may advise taking a non-barbiturate sedative for a short period, but this is something you will need to discuss with him.

Biofeedback

Biofeedback is a revolutionary technique, developed over the last 20 years, which promotes awareness of the effects of stress and strain and how these can lead to stress-related disease, by measuring physical responses to stress. Through the use of specialized electronic metering and other devices, subtle, normally undetectable physiological changes are identified and related to conditions of stress and tension.

Appropriate metering instruments measure and monitor certain physiological indicators, especially skin resistance, perspiration, body temperature and brain wave patterns and rhythms, all of which are linked to levels of arousal in the nervous system, retained tension in the muscles, and states of arousal and stress in the functioning of the brain. Electrodes attached to the body and fed into the biofeedback machine indicate the various physiological effects by means of a light or buzzer: as the user seeks consciously to control his or her stress, the light dims or buzzer quietens, indicating the measure of success.

Biofeedback is of great positive value in monitoring and controlling personal stress levels and achieving relaxation, enhanced self-awareness and greater well-being. It can be applied professionally by doctors as an invaluable alternative to drug therapy; to augment the intuitive approach of the psychothera-pist; and to monitor those practising transcendental meditation (see page 106). Its processes can also be easily mastered by self-users – some machines, widely available in the USA, are no larger than pocket size.

Audio Ltd (see chapter 10) design, manufacture and market a comprehensive range of biofeedback monitoring equipment, including an electrical skin-resistance meter; skin temperature meter; pulse computer; electro-myograph; electro-encephalo-graph; psychelitic stimulator and therapeutic strobe.

The Awakened Mind, the centre founded by C. Maxwell Cade, world-recognized authority on biofeedback, runs courses and classes (see chapter 10).

'Alternative' remedies

In recent years increasing numbers of people have found relief from a variety of disorders and illnesses in alternative methods of health care. More information about these can be obtained from the Institute for Complementary Medicine (see chapter 10) which exists to ensure that the best possible natural health treatments are made available to patients on the same terms as conventional medicine. Therapies may replace conventional medical methods (in which case they are described as 'alternative') or may be practised alongside orthodox medicine, when they are described as 'complementary'. Among the techniques which are particularly helpful in coping with stress are acupuncture, acupressure and aromatherapy.

Acupuncture

The principle behind acupuncture, a traditional method of treatment practised by the Chinese since ancient times, is that the vital energy balance in the body is of crucial importance: the life-force (which the Chinese call *chi*) must circulate freely and without interruption round the meridians, the channels in the body along which the energy circulates (each meridian refers to a particular organ). Needles are inserted into specific points in the body, which may bear no relation to the site of experienced symptoms of pain, but which command the general energy flow of the entire meridian.

Acupuncture is a complex, vitalistic system of healing based on treating the patient as a whole – body and mind – to locate the cause of the complaint – which may be physical or mental – in terms of energy imbalance and breakdown. Once the natural energy flow is restored, body and mind return to a state of balance and harmony. Acupuncture can even help break addiction to drugs, alcohol and smoking, by removing and resolving the stresses that caused the addiction in the first place, and play a significant part in stress-control and treatment generally.

If you are considering taking a course of acupuncture it is extremely important to go to a fully qualified, registered practician – apply in the first instance to the British Medical Acupuncture Society and the Council for Acupuncture (see chapter 10).

Acupressure

This is a deep finger massage over the acupuncture points, applied in the direction of the flow of the meridians, to stimulate those points at which the energy flow is blocked. Like acupuncture, acupressure can successfully treat a variety of stress-related disorders: these include arthritis, neck, shoulder and back pain, migraine, asthma and insomnia. It can help in the treatment of high blood pressure and of angina, where there is a deficiency in the blood supply to the heart muscle.

Aromatherapy

Aromatherapy combines the use of essential oils derived from flowers, fruits, herbs and spices, with massage. Aromatherapy is believed to have a favourable effect on both the immune and nervous systems, as well as rebalancing the body's natural energies. It can be used to treat skin disorders and digestive problems, tension headaches and muscular stiffness, and is powerfully effective in the treatment of depression, anxiety and stress. Among the specific anti-stress antidotes offered by aromatherapeutic oils are jasmine, fennel, hyssop and orange blossom.

For more information on trained aromatherapists, send a self-addressed stamped envelope to the International Federation of Aromatherapists (see chapter 10). For products which you can use at home, available through mail order, phone the Aromatherapy Association on 01-371 0465.

Exercise and stress relief

Physical exercise is of tremendous value in coping with stress, using up excess energy, burning off the potentially toxic nor-adrenalin, and leaving you feeling calmer and more in control. The general sense of well-being experienced after taking exercise follows the increase in circulation, heart activity, breathing and general metabolic rate. Regular exercise keeps the joints supple and the muscles relaxed, dispelling the stiffness and rigidity which are often the after-effect of the stress of everyday living.

Exercising also leaves you mentally as well as physically stronger, and more resilient and able to cope. It's significant that the more exercise you take, the less you will experience mental fatigue, which is very common in those suffering from stress.

Fitness at work

Business companies are increasingly emphasizing physical fitness in their stress-management policies. Many big firms, working together with specially qualified stress consultants, have already installed in-house fitness schemes and have found that these have resulted in reduced absenteeism and staff turnover, increased worker satisfaction and ability to cope better with job stresses.

Health clubs

For many people, taking exercise and keeping fit has become even more of a pleasure through joining one of the proliferation of health clubs now offering membership and the chance to exercise in pleasant surroundings with a sociable atmosphere. Many of these clubs offer a wide choice of exercise – gym, aerobics, weight-lifting, for instance – and offer a special fitness assessment and personalized programme with specially qualified staff, as well as a wide range of therapies and treatments to promote a more relaxed and therefore more positive self-image. In big cities in particular more and more people are making regular visits to the health club as an essential part of their routine, and there couldn't be a better or more enjoyable way of coping with stress. Some clubs with sophisticated hi-tech facilities can seem expensive, but the membership may also seem a small price to pay for taking such positive action to keep harmful stress out of your life!

Yoga

The Eastern philosophy of yoga emphasizes the partnership of mental and physical discipline to achieve total fulfilment and control. In Hatha Yoga, the type most commonly practised in the West, body fitness is acquired by the use of a series of postures or *asanas*, practised regularly and intended to massage the internal organs.

Yoga is a way of life for its true students, who are expected to follow a code of special ethics, and it is far, far more than just a way of keeping fit, as is sometimes thought in the West. However, Hatha Yoga exercises learned from a qualified teacher and practised regularly in class, or at home, can do much to achieve a healthy body and quiet mind – an ideal partnership for handling adverse stress.

T'ai Chi

Like yoga, T'ai Chi is an ancient Eastern discipline, originating in China and evolving over many centuries. Based on Taoist philosophy, it is concerned with stabilizing and harmonizing the ever-fluctuating rhythmic energies (the Yin and Yang) of the personality and balancing the various forces in the body to promote the flow of the *chi*, or life-force. This is achieved through a special art of gentle yet dynamic movements. Slow and dancelike, unlike the more strenuous, held postures of yoga, these ebb and flow continuously, following the rhythms of life itself. Exercise is just part of the total discipline and spiritual healing process of T'ai Chi, but can do much to improve posture and muscle toning, producing a high degree of relaxation, strength and alertness.

The specialized exercises of yoga and T'ai Chi can be taught on a one-to-one basis, or, more usually, collectively, in a class environment. Whichever, they require a fully trained instructor, and need to be carried out on a regular basis. And the same applies to all forms of exercise, either within the framework of everyday routine, or as a special activity: for any exercise to be really effective, it is important to go gently at first and build up a routine gradually.

Choice of exercise

For maximum overall stress-reduction benefit, continuous exercise such as swimming, walking and cycling is frequently recommended rather than a vigorous stop-go activity like tennis, squash or sprinting. Exercise which does not contain a competitive element is obviously less likely to generate stress of its own, and if it can be done in the open air, where its benefit combines with that of oxygen intake, this is ideal. Walking is an excellent form of exercise for everyday purposes, increasing the oxygen flow, strengthening the heart, keeping blood pressure low and joints supple, and helping to work off weight: so try to build a walk into your daily programme in some way or other – take a brisk stroll at lunchtime, perhaps, or make a point of getting off the bus a stop or two earlier on your way home.

Exercise routines

A simple routine constructed round 'clench-and-let-go' exercises can be very effective for releasing stress in a variety of everyday situations. These exercises work by what is called 'reciprocal innovation': voluntary muscular contraction is followed by relaxation.

1 Sit quietly, eyes closed. Clench both fists and hold them clenched for 15 seconds. Then relax them and feel the tension drain away from your arm muscles. Repeat twice.

2 Hunch your shoulders for 15 seconds, bringing them right up towards your ears. Relax, then repeat twice.

3 Now smile as widely as you can, trying to make the smile stretch right across your face: hold the smile for 15 seconds, then relax. Repeat twice.

4 Push up your eyebrows so that you look really surprised. Hold, then relax. Repeat twice.

5 Finally, screw up your eyes as tightly as you can, then relax. Repeat twice.

The same principle can be extended to build up a more elaborate routine, which would be an ideal way to unwind on getting home after an exhausting day. For maximum effectiveness, wear loose clothing and do the exercises in a quiet, dimly lit room, either lying on a bed, sofa or on the floor with cushions, or stretched out in a comfortable armchair:

1 Screw up your toes slowly, hold briefly, then relax.

2 Gently pull up your toes towards your head; hold briefly, then relax.

3 Stretch out your legs to tighten your calf muscles; hold briefly, then relax and take a short rest.

4 Push your knees together, to tighten the thigh muscles. Hold, then relax.

5 Pull in the muscles in your behind, then relax.

6 Push out your stomach, making it as full as you can, hold and relax. Now pull in the muscles in the opposite direction, hold and relax.

7 Apply the exercises for the toes in steps 1 and 2 to your hands.

8 Pull your shoulder blades closely together gently; hold and relax.

9 Shrug your shoulders, hold and relax.

10 Turn your head from side to side, then push it back gently, holding and then relaxing after each movement.

Deep breathing exercise

Under stress, breathing becomes short and shallow, with the oxygen intake considerably reduced. This tendency can be countered by developing special deep breathing techniques, filling the lower half of the lungs first and using the rib-cage and diaphragm muscles to do so. Test that you are doing this correctly by resting your fingers against the bottom of the rib-cage and breathing in – your fingers should draw apart. Hold the breath for a few seconds, then breathe out slowly and rhythmically, feeling the muscles relax as you do so. Follow this breathing pattern when you do other exercises, and use deep breathing to relax in specially stress-prone situations – before an exam or interview, for instance, or after a shock or row.

Passive remedies

Massage is one of the most effective physical remedies for stress. By stimulating the blood flow it reduces muscular tension, and is particularly good for specially stress-prone areas of the body, such as back, neck and shoulders. A full body massage by a trained massage therapist offers guaranteed stress relief, especially if taken on a regular basis.

Massage can also be very effective at home, between partners – the sense of physical contact in itself reduces stress and creates a feeling of calm and trust, and this can extend to the person carrying out the massage as well as the recipient. Some childcare experts advocate the use of massage as a way of soothing babies and consolidating the bonding process with parents.

Baths: Sauna and Turkish baths are a pleasant way to relax and rid yourself of stress and tension. At home, warm, relaxing baths (as opposed to bracing showers), especially if enhanced by soothing therapeutic oils, are an ideal way of shedding the day's pressures.

Body awareness

Learn to 'listen' to your body, to detect signs of stress at an early stage, when you can take relevant action. Frowning, involuntarily clenching fists, sitting in a hunched, uncomfortable position, or tensely on the edge of a chair, shallow breathing, teeth-grinding, walking compulsively up and down, moving a crossed leg rapidly up and down, are all easily identifiable stress symptoms. Be aware of your posture in everyday situations and be prepared to correct it when necessary – for example, if you find yourself gripping the telephone receiver unnecessarily tightly during a telephone conversation, or the steering wheel of the car when driving.

The Alexander Technique

Through the Alexander Technique, relaxation is achieved by a combination of gentle manual guidance and verbal instruction. The Technique is based on awareness of balance, posture and movement in everyday activity, helping students to recognize previously unnoticed tensions and to distinguish between necessary and unnecessary tensions and effort. In the Alexander Technique, posture is of crucial importance – the way we support and balance our bodies against the pull of gravity as we go about our daily lives. According to Alexander, it is possible to organize this support and balance mechanism without undue effort by a system of natural postural reflexes. For these to be effective, it is vital that they should work freely, and this is what the teachers of the Technique help their students to achieve, unravelling the muscular tensions and patterns of distortion which have become fixed in the body as a result of emotional and physical stresses and strains, and encouraging the natural reflexes to work again as efficiently as they can be seen to do in small children. Movement, breathing, circulation and digestion are all improved through the Alexander Technique, whose teachers show students how to help the natural mechanisms function more freely by learning to project simple messages from the brain to the body.

All lessons are individual and usually last 30–40 minutes: for best results, a course of 20–30 lessons spread over 3–5 months is recommended. Qualified teachers' addresses may be obtained from the Society of Teachers of the Alexander Technique (see chapter 10).

Bodywork

Treating your body well will pay immeasurable dividends in terms of stress reduction. The fitter you are, the more relaxed you will be, and this will be reflected not just in how you feel, but how you look too – relaxation is one of the keys to natural good looks. One very pleasant way of keeping stress at bay is to try to set aside a day on a regular basis which you can use as a kind of home health farm, including a massage, facial, fasting (see page 101), and generally relaxing.

Stress and sex

Good sex in a secure and happy relationship, like any form of in-depth, intense personal communication between people who care for each other, can act as one of the most concentrated, powerful and effective ways of relieving stress and achieving total relaxation. As well as bringing physical pleasure and satisfaction, loving, well-balanced sex enhances a relationship emotionally, creating a deep sense of closeness and togetherness, the perfect antidote to negatively stressful feelings.

Yet sex may also be a source of stresses and strains in its own right. For example, it can cause problems if instead of complementing other expressions of togetherness in a relationship, such as companionship, friendship, shared interests, it assumes excessive, even exclusive importance. Or if there is not total mutual trust, sexual jealousy of a particularly painful nature can develop – one of the surest ways of causing relations to deteriorate. Or a couple may experience sexual difficulties based on mutual incompatibilities or different expectations, for example of frequency or type of intercourse, or the degree of importance respectively attached to sex. Such problems easily assume overwhelming proportions, and are a common source of marital stress generally (see page 33).

Like other problems within marriage or any close and permanent relationship, talking about them may do much to release the stress element and open up a path towards finding a solution. It may be enough for a couple to talk to each other and devise their own ways of overcoming their specific problems – there is a vast literature on the subject to help. Marriage guidance organizations (see chapter 10) offer valuable assistance – some provide special sex therapy counselling for couples – and sexual dysfunction or psychosexual clinics are attached to some hospitals, health centres and family planning clinics. This is also an area in which GPs are increasingly able and willing to offer counselling.

Equally, sexual relations can be adversely affected by quite separate, distinct types of stress. Obviously, this is especially likely to be the case if, for whatever reason, a relationship is undergoing difficulties elsewhere, but other stress problems affecting one or both partners – especially fatigue caused by overwork, or worries in other areas of life – can easily cause sex to deteriorate, bringing a general loss of libido, and perhaps impotence and premature ejaculation in a man, and frigidity in a woman. Body changes, too, affect sexual desire and performance as we get older. It is important to be aware of all these possibilities and their potential effect on your sex life: as with all forms of stress, awareness and understanding are the best foundation from which to cope, rather than letting events take you by surprise.

Pre-menstrual tension

Many women experience upsetting emotional or physical problems during the second half of their menstrual cycle, when the womb lining prepared by the body for a fertilized egg is shed as a period if conception has not taken place. PMT can contribute to sexual problems, making some women temporarily lose their libido (although in others it may have the reverse effect). In itself, PMT is a cause of acute distress in sufficient numbers of women for it to be taken increasingly seriously by GPs, most of whom are able to offer helpful advice – and special PMT clinics are also run by some hospitals; advice can likewise be obtained from family planning clinics. Causes of PMT include:

☐ Insufficient supply of the progesterone hormone produced by the ovaries.

☐ Disturbed balance between the progesterone and oestrogen hormones.

☐ Disturbance of the body's ability to absorb B-group vitamins.

Obviously you are likely to suffer more from PMT if you are experiencing other stress-related problems, or are not eating a healthy, well-balanced diet.

As a basis for coping with PMT, it is useful to be aware of the types of symptom commonly experienced, which can be both physical and emotional:

Physical symptoms
☐ A bloated feeling, caused by water retention
☐ Weight increase
☐ Swollen, tender breasts

- ☐ Distended abdomen
- ☐ Impaired coordination
- ☐ Headache and nausea
- ☐ Fatigue
- ☐ Poor sleep
- ☐ Food cravings, especially for sweet or salty foods
- ☐ Spots on face and body
- ☐ Tendency for hair to be greasy

Emotional symptoms
- ☐ Mood changes, sometimes quite abrupt
- ☐ Strong feelings of tension and irritability
- ☐ Poor concentration
- ☐ Forgetfulness
- ☐ Weepiness
- ☐ Touchiness

Keys to coping with PMT

■ Try to minimize stressful events in the second half of your menstrual cycle, and to avoid getting overtired at this time.

■ Look after your general health and diet (see page 97).

■ Wear loose-fitting, comfortable clothes.

■ Relax by taking some form of gentle but effective exercise – a walk, for instance.

■ Consult your doctor about taking a course of vitamin B_6.

■ Consult your doctor, too, about the use of diuretics to relieve water retention (these are usually advisable in the short rather than the long term).

If you feel really bad, ask about taking progesterone.

Stress and the menopause

The menopause, or 'change of life' as it's commonly called, undoubtedly generates a great deal of stress in many women in the mid-years of their lives. Equally, it is commonly surrounded by myth and old wives' tales, and it is not just the physical and emotional aspects of the menopause itself which are necessarily exclusively responsible for stress – other major changes in life patterns which so often coincide with it can be equally stressful: for example, a seeming loss of supportive family life and sense of direction, with children growing up and leaving home, or a husband at the peak of his career and preoccupied with his work.

The facts of the menopause are: between the ages of 45–55 the egg follicles in a woman's ovaries gradually disappear, and reduced amounts of the oestrogen hormone are released during each menstrual cycle. The pattern and flow of her periods change until they finally cease completely. This is a time of hormonal turbulence second only to puberty, with progressive oestrogen deficiency, absence of progesterone, and rise in pituitary hormones.

'Hot flushes' – a sudden feeling of heat which spreads over the face and body – are the most familiar symptom associated with the menopause: headaches and palpitations are also common, as are unpredictable swings of mood, depression and a feeling of uselessness and lack of purpose.

Positive attitude of mind can do a tremendous amount to counter the stress of the menopause, and women experiencing it now benefit from a much greater awareness of its problems and sympathy with them on the part of most medical practitioners, who can offer helpful, constructive advice.

Keys to coping with the menopause

■ Remind yourself that this is a temporary natural phase shared by all women, which will pass.

■ Be aware of what's happening in your body.

■ Keep up interests and develop new ones, to avoid dwelling on negative thoughts.

■ Don't make the mistake of equating the menopause with loss of sexual attractiveness – this just isn't so!

■ Watch your diet and take plenty of exercise to counter weight gain.

■ Talk to your doctor. He may suggest oestrogen tablets to cope with hot flushes, or perhaps some hormone replacement therapy, which many women find does wonders for reducing stress and enhancing a sense of well-being during the menopause.

Stress-free diet

Paying attention to what and how you eat, to ensure a well-balanced, healthy diet, is one of the most positive steps it's possible to take in order to protect your body against some of the most harmful effects of damaging stress, and equip yourself physically for stress-resistance.

One of the aspirational physical images most consistently conveyed by the media is that of slimness, a concept which is projected not just as healthy and physically attractive, but closely linked to the ideal of success which has assumed such prime importance in Western society. Acquiring and maintaining a slim body, like anything else if taken to extremes and allowed to get out of proportion, can itself become a source of stress. Obsession with a stereotyped body image does not make sense as everybody's physical make-up is different, and certainly resorting to drastic measures like crash diets cannot be recommended. But being happy about your body weight and the trim outline that goes with this is good for your health generally as well as your looks, and on both counts will do a lot to help you maintain a buoyant, stress-free outlook on life.

It's a good idea to check your weight regularly and review your eating habits from time to time if necessary – as well, of course, as taking regular exercise as discussed on page 89. It may be useful to bear in mind the recommended daily calorie intake for lifestyles led at different ages: for example, a middle-aged man leading a sedentary lifestyle will require about 2500 calories; if moderately active, approximately 2800; if very active, 3350. Women between the ages of 18 and 54 in most occupations usually require 2150 calories or up to 2500 if very active; but aged over 55 with a more sedentary lifestyle, between 1700 and 1900.

Calories provide energy which if not used up naturally converts into fat, hence the value of calorie-counting to maintain the right proportion of energy intake. Equally important, however, is ensuring that you eat a well-balanced variety of foods to supply your body with all the nutrients in the form of protein, carbohydrate, vitamins and minerals that it requires to function well. If you are suffering from stress, it could be that your diet is deficient in the essential B-complex vitamins: insufficient intake of vitamin B_1, for example, can affect the functioning of the heart and nervous system (common symptoms of this are a sensation of tingling and pins and needles).

The following chart shows the foods containing the B-group of vitamins:

B-group vitamins	*Principal source*
vitamin B_1 (thiamine)	wholegrain cereals
vitamin B_2 (riboflavin)	milk, cheese, eggs, meat, offal, yeast extract
vitamin B_3 (nicotinic acid, niacin)	fish, meat, offal, wholegrain cereals, pulses
vitamin B_6 (pyridoxine)	cereals, meat, fruit, leafy and other vegetables
vitamin B_{12} (cyanocobalamin and folic acid)	liver and green vegetables

Foods rich in pure energy are valuable in a stress-free diet. These include:
  □ fruit, for its natural sugar and fibre content
  □ vegetables, especially green vegetables, for their high concentration of vitamins and minerals
  □ honey, an excellent substitute for refined sugar
  □ nuts, pulses and cereals, naturally high in fibre and good for ensuring regular body functions (constipation, for example, can cause uncomfortable stress)

Eating as many raw foods as possible – lots of salads and crunchy vegetable crudités, fresh and dried fruits, for example – is also highly recommended as part of any healthy diet. Try to get into the habit of starting a meal with a salad or crudités.

Top of the list of foods to avoid are those with a high fat, salt or sugar content, or which contain artificial additives (get into the habit of checking product labels for these). Fatty foods contribute to high cholesterol levels in the blood, thus increasing the risk of high blood pressure, which is often associated with stress: doctors treating high blood pressure or hypertension also recommend cutting down on salt and on caffeine, present in coffee, tea and cola drinks, which by triggering the release of the hormone adrenaline can result in an over-stimulated system. Foods high in saturated fats, particularly red meat and full-fat dairy products, clog the arteries with fatty deposits – one of the prime causes of coronary disease.

Fatty foods, like those high in refined carbohydrate, especially sugar and sweets, are also often responsible for putting on excess weight; and obesity is of course one of the major factors contributing to a greater risk of heart disease. Medical research indicates, too, that excessive carbohydrate intake also releases serotonin, a nerve messenger instrumental in causing anxiety and tension.

Nearly a third of all deaths in the UK in people aged under 75 are the result of heart disease, which can of course number stress among its causes. Looking after your heart, and doing so from an early age, is among the best protective measures you can take against suffering later in life from angina, a heart attack or coronary thrombosis, which occurs when a sudden, severe blockage – usually a blood clot – in one of the coronary arteries cuts off the blood supply to part of the heart muscle.

Keys to a healthy heart
The following suggestions for watching what you and your family eat will help you to ensure that you do not become a coronary casualty, as well as enhancing your general sense of well-being (remember that smoking and insufficient exercise are also key contributory factors to heart disease).

■ Choose skimmed or semi-skimmed milk in preference to full-cream, and low-fat yoghurt and cheeses, such as cottage cheese and Edam (both of these relatively low-fat cheeses make delicious fillings for healthy sandwiches made with wholemeal bread spread with polyunsaturated margarine or low-fat spread instead of butter).

- Eat more low-fat, high-protein fish and chicken.

- When you buy meat, look for lean-choice roasting joints, stewing steak or mince. Many supermarkets now make a point of labelling meat products with their fat content.

- Remove all visible fat from meat.

- Skim all excess fat from gravies and stocks.

- Grill rather than fry.

- Use minimum added fat in cooking: for example, use roasting bags for a joint of meat.

- Cut down on sugar: go easy on sweet pastries, cakes, biscuits and confectionery, and do without sugar in hot drinks, or use an artificial sweetener.

- Avoid greasy, salty snacks like potato chips and crisps: cut back on your use of salt in cooking, and make imaginative use of herbs, natural flavour-enhancers, instead.

Keys to good digestion
Stress levels can be affected for better or worse not only by what you eat, but by *how* you eat. Here are some ideas to help you and your family derive the maximum benefit from your diet.

- Try to keep to reasonably regular mealtimes.

- Don't go for too long without a meal.

- Avoid rushed meals.

- Make mealtimes reasonably leisurely, sociable occasions.

- Eat slowly, chewing food well to aid the digestion.

- Also as an aid to good digestion, allow yourself some time to relax after a meal.

- Acquire the habit of eating little and often.
- Avoid eating heavy meals late at night.

Fasting

Depending on whether your doctor feels it is right for you and your lifestyle – always check on this first – getting into the habit of fasting regularly, say a day a month, can do wonders for keeping stress levels down. Properly conducted, fasting releases toxic substances and rests and cleanses the system, lowers high blood pressure and cholesterol levels, reduces tension – and helps you lose weight!

However, fasting does *not* mean cutting out eating altogether while carrying on as normal. To fast properly and beneficially, set aside a day when you can be sure of no interruptions, and use it to relax without eating, but making sure that you sip plenty of mineral water or herb tea throughout your fast: you will need to take in 2.25 litres/4 pints of liquid during the day. Herb teas or tisanes, especially camomile or feverfew, have a particularly soothing, relaxing effect, and make admirable substitutes for ordinary tea or coffee when you are watching your stress levels.

Stress and smoking

The nicotine in cigarettes is a mood-altering substance which helps cope with stress superficially by providing relaxation at moments of tension – for example, during a difficult business phone call or at a party where you are meeting new people – and seemingly improving concentration when you have a job to get done against the clock. But this is only superficial. In reality, in body terms, nicotine increases the pulse rate and raises the blood pressure, while the carbon monoxide content of cigarette smoke reduces the levels of oxygen in the blood. Thus the heart has to work harder on less oxygen, and the smoke also accelerates the furring up of the coronary arteries: it is this potentially lethal combination which makes cigarette smoking such a significant cause, or contributory cause, of both heart disease and lung cancer: a high price indeed to pay for temporary apparent respite from stress.

Unfortunately, nicotine is also an addictive substance, and

kicking the habit can pose real problems for smokers who decide to do the only sensible thing and give up. It's ironic that while smoking itself sets the physiological processes of stress in motion, giving it up can also be highly stressful. *Really wanting* to stop smoking is the best starting-point for doing so, and one of the best ways to convince yourself is to be aware of the frightening statistic that cigarette smoking can actually double your risk of dying from a heart attack – in the case of heavy smokers, possibly at a relatively young age – and that men and women are equally at risk.

Keys to giving up smoking

■ Convince yourself that this is the only course to take.

■ Change your routine to avoid situations where you know you usually smoke – meeting other smoking friends at the pub, for example. It will probably only be necessary to follow this course for a few weeks.

■ Take each day as it comes, and regard each successfully cigarette-free day as something to be really proud of, perhaps rewarding yourself with a treat.

■ Make full use of the 'no smoking' areas which are increasingly being made available in offices, cinemas, theatres and on public transport.

■ Find other activities to substitute for smoking, especially things to do with your hands, like knitting, embroidery, dressmaking, carpentry and other DIY.

■ Don't worry about putting on weight, which often puts smokers off giving up: you won't if you follow a sensible diet, as outlined on pages 97–9, and keep a supply of low-calorie nibbles like carrot or celery sticks handy to eat when you get the urge for a cigarette.

■ Remind yourself of all the money you are saving that went up in smoke before!

■ Enjoy the better general health you will experience – fewer colds and infections, for example.

■ Enjoy the greater sense of fitness and well-being – being able to run faster, for example, or not getting out of breath when you climb the stairs.

Finally knowing that you have given up for good will make the initial decision seem like the best you ever made, but it's no good denying that withdrawing from smoking, as from any addictive drug, can be a stressful process, and you may find one of the organizations which exist specifically to help people in your situation useful – details can be found in chapter 10.

Stress and alcohol

Reaching for a drink, like reaching for a cigarette, is a very common reaction to varying degrees of stress, from social shyness to major life problems. Drinking well within the limits, in sensible moderation, is sociable and can probably actually help alleviate mild stress, but it's when it becomes a firm habit, an established reflex, that warning signals should start to sound.

Most of the alcohol we drink is rapidly absorbed into the bloodstream: nearly all of it has to be burned up by the liver (at the rate of 1 unit of alcohol per hour) and the rest leaves the body through the pores of the skin or as urine. *Excess* alcohol produces excess hydro-cortisone and other stress-related hormones, so that after the initial feeling of relaxation conveyed by a drink, a state of apparent stimulation follows.

It is for just this sensation of combined relaxation and stimulation that most people drink, but contrary to popular belief alcohol is not in fact a stimulant – it's a depressant, in the sense that it depresses certain functions of the brain, which can affect coordination, concentration, judgement and self-control. Drinking alcohol may seem to alleviate stress to begin with, but excess consumption can quickly create stress problems of its own, for example by interfering with sleep patterns, leading to hangovers, or causing accidents, and, when taken to extremes, resulting in severe addiction which can lead to stresses of its own, such as problems at work, deterioration of home life, loss of self-esteem, all probably of a much more serious nature than those the drink was first intended to relieve.

It has been suggested that men are more likely to drink to help them cope with problems at work (or with lack of work), and women because of problems in relationships. Whichever, it is a firmly established fact that alcohol abuse is no long-term remedy for stress, but rather, just the opposite.

Excess drinking can harm the body in a number of ways, and of these, those specially related to stress are high blood pressure, stomach ulcers and problems with the muscles and nervous system. Others include hepatitis (inflammation of the liver), cirrhosis (permanent scarring of the liver) and some forms of cancer. In the light of these hard facts it is very well worth taking a close, really objective look at your drinking habits, to make yourself aware not only of just how much you drink on a regular basis, but when you do so. If, for example, you consistently mix yourself a stiff gin and tonic when you get home from the office, and after a really hard day there's a tendency to make this two, then three . . . it would be a good idea to make yourself a mug of tea, or pour yourself a refreshing tumbler of mineral water topped with ice cubes and a twist of lemon instead.

As far as quantity is concerned, it could be enlightening and valuable to note in your diary how many alcohol units you consume during the course of a week, based on the calculation:

1 alcohol unit $= \frac{1}{2}$ pint beer; a glass of wine; a single measure of spirits.

This exercise is only worthwhile if you are really honest with yourself! Count up your total units for the week and then compare it with the recommended 'safe' alcohol consumption level, which should carry no long-term health risk:

Men: up to 21 units

Women: up to 14 units

(Women are more easily affected by drink than men because 10 per cent more of men's body weight is made up of water, which dilutes alcohol.) Drinking over 36 units for men, and over 22 for women, means that damage to health is likely.

Remember – you won't just be doing your overall health a lot of good, you will also be avoiding the dual error made in drinking to relieve stress: failing to find a reliable long-term remedy for stress, and instead, building up a new set of stressors.

NINE

STATE OF MIND
Stress Remedies

Mind and body are closely related in stress terms, and physical relaxation, as described in the previous chapter, can never be fully achieved in a state of mental tension or anxiety. To cope satisfactorily with stress, it is necessary to relax mentally as well, and there are a number of special techniques which you can develop to help yourself do this.

Meditation

The use of meditation in learning to control the mind and thus achieve a deep sense of calm, accompanied by enhanced inner awareness, was part of Buddha's teaching, and is an important aspect of Buddhist and other Eastern philosophies. In this original context meditation has a profound spiritual significance; in Western society, for whose benefit a number of different schools of meditation have adapted their styles and techniques, the emphasis is laid particularly on the deep and satisfying state of overall well-being that is achieved by practising meditation successfully.

That meditation is of special value in reducing stress is confirmed by the metabolic and EEG changes which have been noted during its practice; the heart rate slows down and the brainwave pattern indicates a mental state that combines complete repose with total alertness; at the same time the consumption of oxygen and the depth of breathing decrease, and the muscles relax.

Most practitioners of meditation find two daily sessions of 10–15 minutes ideal – one in the morning before embarking on the day, the other to bring it to a restful and relaxed close. But once the techniques have been acquired, meditating for just a few minutes can achieve instant reduction in stress levels, and a generally unstressed condition will extend beyond the actual periods of meditation.

Like physical exercise, relaxation through meditation needs to be progressive, and must also be properly learned, either in a class or group, or on a one-to-one basis with a qualified practitioner. As well as those offered by individual schools of meditation, many adult education centres provide meditation classes. Of the former, the best-known is probably the school of Transcendental Meditation, founded by Maharishi Mahesh Yogi in India in the 1950s, which now has a virtually worldwide following. The aim of TM, as it is commonly known, is to reach the source of thought, in its purest and simplest state, within the quiet depths of the mind. This is achieved by concentrating exclusively on the inner repetition of a personal ritual word or *mantra*, which rids the mind of all irrelevant thought.

Hypnosis

Like meditation, hypnosis creates a state of altered awareness, which can be directed effectively towards the control of stress. The person under hypnosis responds to suggestions proffered by the therapist: for example, he or she may be asked to picture stressful situations and ways in which to deal with them effectively. These suggested remedies then stay with the person outside the periods of treatment, to be made use of as and when required. Hypnosis can thus be highly effective in controlling stress, especially particularly acute manifestations of it, but will depend for its success on degree of suggestibility – some people respond to hypnosis much better than others.

Autogenics

Autogenics, as originally developed by Dr Wolfgang Luthe in Canada, are a series of mental exercises designed to help 'switch off' from stress by means of passive concentration. Once the basic techniques of autogenics have been acquired, they can be safely adapted to all sorts of situations in everyday life.

Autogenic training offers general improvement in mental well-being, and physical benefits such as lowering of blood pressure, and even reduction in blood cholesterol levels. Autogenic exercises can be particularly effective in curing insomnia, and dealing with examination nerves, jet lag and work stress. Anyone can practise autogenics – no special clothing or equipment are required other than a comfortable chair, ideally in a quiet room.

Autogenic training teaches the repetition of a series of phrases designed to induce deep relaxation. Examples of these include:

- □ My hands and arms are heavy and warm.
- □ My feet and legs are heavy and warm.
- □ My abdomen is warm and comfortable.
- □ My breathing is deep and even.
- □ My forehead is cool.
- □ When I open my eyes, I will remain relaxed and refreshed.

It is essential to learn autogenics from qualified experts – details of the Centre for Autogenic Training can be found in chapter 10.

The common-sense of stress

It may help to maintain your general stress-awareness if you refer back to the 20 ground rules or guidelines listed in chapter 1 (see pages 13–14). It is also enormously valuable to familiarize yourself with the specific things which you as an individual find stressful – anything from frustration within a relationship which seems to be going nowhere, an inability to let the past go, or allowing past experiences to build up into sources of anger, to the harassed feeling we all experience when there are too many demands on our time.

One very practical and useful approach to stress-assessment of this kind is to keep a detailed 'time-management' diary, noting the various ways in which your time was spent.

- □ Getting ready to go to work
- □ Getting the children off to school
- □ In the kitchen
- □ On the telephone
- □ On household chores
- □ Shopping
- □ In meetings
- □ Travelling
- □ Taking physical exercise

- ☐ Relaxing
- ☐ In conversation with family and friends
- ☐ Sleeping

By listing on the entry for each day exactly how you used your time, you will be building up excellent 'source material' to enable you to use your time most effectively – which in itself is a strong defence against harmful, negative stress.

Taking regular stock of your own stress levels is the ideal complement to relaxation techniques in equipping yourself mentally and emotionally to cope with stress. Thinking of how you may affect others – family, friends or work colleagues in particular – through stress is also important: for example, being aware of how excessively motivated, overactive people can so easily become sources of stress to others as well as to themselves, is a good way of ensuring that you do not inadvertently become the exhausting kind of person who quite literally cannot stop. In your relations with others, you can reduce stress by not taking offence easily and generally trying to see a situation from the other person's point of view as well as your own – it's an attitude which creates not only good relations, but a richer view of life.

Talking treatment

The opportunity to communicate is one of the most welcome aspects of good relations with others. Just talking through a problem with a trusted relative or friend can do a very great deal to take the stress out of it; and those people who belong to any kind of religious community will find talking to their minister or co-believers particularly therapeutic.

However, such opportunities do not always present themselves when most required, and for a variety of reasons it may not always be feasible to talk in depth with people you know personally about problems or situations which you feel may be causing you undesirable stress. When this is the case, you may feel that you could benefit from some specialist professional help, such as that offered by counselling.

Counselling may be in special areas which are notoriously stress-prone, such as marital difficulties or coping with bereavement – many of the different organizations listed in chapter 10 offer specialist counselling in one form or another. Or you may find that talking to a qualified counsellor on more general terms is useful. Either way, recognition of the value of counselling is certainly constantly on the increase: to give just one example, physiotherapists are now learning counselling skills to give extra emotional support to their patients during treatment.

A counsellor's main task is to enable the 'client' (the word is always used in preference to 'patient') to consider alternatives, both for ways of approaching situations and for thinking about and tackling problems. It is not the role of the counsellor to give direct advice, but to point out possibilities, within a context of support and acceptance.

A sympathetic counsellor, who may well have had direct personal experience of the problems facing his client, can offer invaluable help in finding solutions to difficulties that the client may see as insoluble, and working out coping strategies. In a good counselling session, stresses will be released, and issues clarified.

An important aspect of counselling is for clients to learn to accept themselves as they are, to enable harmful mental stress to be ultimately resolved. The counsellor will help the client see for himself how bad habits have built up, and then discover how best to break them: for example, an ambitious, self-reliant personality is able to learn that success may be just as easily achieved by skilful delegation, while a compulsive worrier may learn to avoid imaginary anxieties by learning self-assertiveness and the use of special relaxation techniques.

Keys to making adjustments

Whether as a result of counselling or not, you may feel that your lifestyle could benefit from some restructuring, to enable you to cope with stress better, and lead a more balanced life. The following pointers might be part of your overall plan.

■ Take an objective look at personal relationships.

■ Plan the work side of your life so as to achieve the right type and amount, in the right conditions, offering a satisfactory degree of job fulfilment.

- Make plenty of room in your life for mental and physical relaxation.

- Keep plenty of space, too, for leisure interests.

Leisure interests

Using your leisure time effectively plays a vital part in stress management. Leisure interests are an essential counterpart to work, and developing them will stand you in very good stead when the time comes for retirement, as discussed in chapter 7.

It is essential to choose hobbies and interests which are right for you, and to regard them as purely leisure activities, rather than treating them like work! It's often a good idea to choose leisure interests which will balance out your job situation in terms of contrast, by providing something in your life which your work cannot. For example, if you have a very active, physically demanding and tiring job, you may find that learning a language in your spare time offers an ideally relaxing yet stimulating contrast. On the other hand, if you have a highly cerebral job, confined to a desk for much of the time, taking regular physical exercise and making a real interest of it – joining a ramblers' group or swimming club, for example – may provide just the right balance.

Certainly any leisure activity which can be shared, through joining a class, club or other type of association, has an extra dimension in terms of stress therapy, offering companionship, social contact and opportunities for meeting new people, all in themselves valuable and enjoyable ways of dissipating harmful stress that comes from loneliness.

By the same token, taking up some voluntary work on behalf of others less fortunate than yourself is not only a thoroughly worthwhile way of doing something constructive to help, but will also indirectly enable you to get your own problems into perspective, while meeting all sorts of people in a variety of situations.

Playing and listening to music, singing – especially in a choir – painting, making pottery, cooking and gardening, are among the most valuable hobbies for keeping stress levels down. Music in particular has unique soothing qualities and ability to lift the spirits. Cooking, like painting, can be highly absorbing, offering plenty of scope for experimentation and creativity, as well as giving a great deal of pleasure in terms of the results: some of the techniques of cookery – kneading bread dough, for example – are especially therapeutic, in the same way that working with clay is.

Gardening is arguably the most highly recommended stress-relieving activity of all. Very importantly, it keeps you in touch with nature and the rhythm of the seasons, which can be all too easily lost sight of while coping with the pressures of modern life; it is excellent exercise, carried out mostly in the fresh air, and endlessly absorbing, offering an infinite variety of tasks. In addition the achievement of having helped beautiful things grow affords great satisfaction. Gardening also offers unrivalled camaraderie based on shared interests, cutting through barriers of class, age and sex. Flower shows at national and local level do of course create considerable competitive stress and tensions generated by unpredictable weather, for instance, but on the whole it must be possible to rate keen gardeners as among the least stressed of people!

Seeing the funny side

Stress is a serious subject, not to be taken lightly, but it is an undeniable fact that a sense of humour and an ability to see the funny side of things can help reduce potential stress in a given situation considerably. Just as a warm smile and offering simple courtesies to others can help immeasurably in relieving everyday frustrations, so laughter is in itself a powerful release of tension.

Research based on group therapy in Sweden, in which participating members meet regularly to exchange funny experiences and share amusing material, has shown that the very act of laughing can make the muscles relax and the stress diminish. So don't forget the value of quite literally laughing the stress away!

TEN

SOURCES OF HELP

The previous chapters have shown how it is possible to develop personal strategies for coping with individual stress levels in a variety of situations which most people experience at some time or other in their lives. These preventive tactics aim to defuse stress before it becomes damaging, and help to make stress work for you rather than against you. However, there may also be times when you feel that it is just not possible to cope alone. At times like these, being aware of the extensive network of societies and organizations which exist specifically to help people cope can be of immense reassurance: most of them offer some form of special counselling geared to specific stress problems.

There is hardly an aspect of stress that is not covered in one way or another by such organizations: marital and family relations; single-parenting; childcare; bereavement; old age and the care of the elderly; drink and smoking problems; stress-related ailments such as back pain, migraine and so on. And there are societies specializing in various forms of stress therapy such as yoga and different relaxation techniques.

This chapter, while necessarily selective, describes the services offered by a number of organizations covering the stress areas discussed in this book, presented for easy reference in the same order as the chapter subjects. Many of them work on a 'self-help' basis, providing counselling and opportunities to discuss and share problems with others who have experienced similar forms of stress: the two are often combined. Depending, of course, on the individual, the support offered can be invaluable; most importantly, by creating the comforting feeling that you are not alone, either in experiencing stress or attempting to come to terms with it – a sure way of building a sound foundation from which to cope.

Stress at Work

Stress Research and Control Centre
Birkbeck College
University of London
Malet Street
London WC1E 7HX
Tel. 01-631 6243

Under the direction of Dr Pat Shipley, the Centre provides Organizational Stress Management Services through which business firms and companies can receive advice on assessing areas and sources of stress and setting up a stress-management policy tailored to their special requirements.

Work Research Unit
ACAS (Advisory Conciliation and Arbitration Service)
St Vincent House
30 Orange Street
London WC2H 7HH
Tel. 01-839 9281/9

The Unit focuses on all human aspects of work, including stress. It has produced a film, *A Better Way of Working*, which offers invaluable insights into ways of creating unstressed conditions in the workplace.

Stress at Home

RELATE (National Marriage Guidance Council)
Herbert Gray College
Little Church Street
Rugby
Warwicks CV21 3AP
Tel. 0788 73241/60811

The London Marriage Guidance Council
76a New Cavendish Street
London W1M 7LB
Tel. 01-580 1087

RELATE offers counselling on all aspects of marital problems, either at headquarters or local counselling centres, to individuals, couples or groups. Individuals and couples will see their counsellor for 1 hour every week for as long as helpful, and are asked to contribute what they can afford towards the cost of maintaining the service. A special sex therapy advisory service is also available. Group counselling may be especially helpful for clients who would like to explore and share their difficulties in a group setting: groups of up to eight clients, with two group leaders, meet for a fixed series of thirty $1\frac{1}{2}$-hour sessions over a year, charges being individually negotiated. Potential group members are offered an initial assessment interview. Contact the Council direct or by referral.

Family Welfare Association
501 Kingsland Road
London E8
Tel. 01-254 6251

The Association deals with all stress issues relating to the individual and the family unit, and will refer callers to its local offices in their area where they can benefit from counselling, GP-related schemes and other social services and special projects.

The Tavistock Institute of Marital Studies
120 Belsize Lane
London NW3 5BA
Tel. 01-435 7111

The Institute maintains three principal activities, all of which closely support and inform each other: psychotherapy for couples; training and consultation for practitioners and managers, with a two-year diploma course in marital psychotherapy; and research and service development. The therapy offered to couples aims to help them discover and implement their own choices. There is an initial consultation, and two therapists are normally assigned to each couple, with partners seen together and separately in regular weekly sessions of 1 hour. There is also a special consultation service available to individuals whose partners are unable or unwilling to attend. Negotiable fees are based on clients' financial circumstances and the cost of providing the service. The Institute's services are in great demand and there is a waiting list, but there is a special consulting service for couples in urgent distress.

National Family Conciliation Council
Shaftesbury Centre
Percy Street
Swindon SN2 2AZ
Tel. 0793 514055

The Council's primary aim is to help couples involved in the process of separation and divorce to reach agreements, or reduce the area or intensity of conflict between them, especially on disputes concerning their children, in both the short and the long term. The service the Council provides can do much to ease the stress of confusion, conflict and lack of communication which often surrounds the breakdown of a marriage and may be intensified by legal proceedings, with adverse effects that may last for many years. The Council encourages couples to meet on neutral ground, with the help of trained conciliators, to explore possibilities of reaching joint decisions that will in particular help them to maintain their joint responsibility as parents and involvement in their children's welfare.

CRUSE
Cruse House
126 Sheen Road
Richmond
Surrey TW9 1UR
Tel. 01-940 4818

Cruse – whose name comes from the Biblical story of the widow's cruse – offers help to all bereaved people, either through links with its headquarters, or local Cruse branches. Its services include counselling, advice and information on practical matters, and opportunities for contact with others in similar situations. There is a Contact List for national members who are widowed and would like to contact other widows and widowers, and regular social meetings are held in the branches.

Exploring Parenthood
41 North Road
London N7 9DP
Tel. 01-607 9647

A national advice and counselling service for parents, which aims to help them find their own way of coping more confidently with the stresses and strains of family life. Easy access to family therapists and counsellors is provided through a telephone advice line and day workshops, where parents can explore their difficulties together with other parents facing similar problems, led by professional counsellors and therapists. Courses are arranged to provide instruction for parent support-group leaders and in-service training for professionals: health visitors, teachers, nursery workers, and so on. It also runs workshops and support groups in a one-parent family programme.

Working Mothers' Association
   77 Holloway Road
   London N7 8JZ
   Tel. 01-700 5771
Through a network of local groups, the Association provides an informal support system for working mothers, assisting parents to make the best choices available in childcare, and offering advice and information to all who combine parenthood with another occupation. The Working Mothers' groups are set up, run and funded independently on a volunteer basis and offer moral support, regular meetings – special 'back-to-work' meetings are held for new or prospective working mothers – and a telephone counselling service. Some have a nanny-sharing register and an emergency register of child-carers or mothers willing to look after an extra child in case of illness.

National Stepfamily Association
   162 Tenison Road
   Cambridge CB1 2DP
   Tel. 0223 460312
The Association helps with all aspects of being in a stepfamily unit. Members are put in touch with local self-help groups and are advised on how to set one up. Mailing lists of relevant literature, and a national list of specialist family therapists, are available. Members receive a quarterly newsletter and free copies of booklets and leaflets. The Association offers a number of specialist

publications designed to help different step-family members, on subjects such as preparing for step-parenthood, teenagers in stepfamilies, becoming a step-grandparent, all stressing the special challenges of being in a step-family and advising on how to cope. A most important feature of the Association's work is the counselling service it provides: most of the counsellors are themselves members of step-families, some are professional family therapists, some specially trained telephone counsellors. Step-families with stress problems may be seen individually or in a group. The Stepfamily Telephone Counselling Service, which is free and confidential, answers callers' needs (adults and children) at moments of crisis, stress or worry. It will refer callers if required for on-going further counselling in local step-family self-help groups.

Gingerbread
35 Wellington Street
London WC2E 7BN
Tel. 01-240 0953
This registered charity for single-parent families has a nationwide network of 300 affiliated self-help groups, offering advice, shared experiences, social contact and joint activities.

National Council for One-Parent Families
255 Kentish Town Road
London NW5 2LX
Tel. 01-267 1361
Provides free advice on all aspects of single-parenting, including legal advice on such matters as custody and maintenance, social security, tax, and housing. It lobbies for a fairer deal for single parents.

OPUS (Organization for Parents Under Stress)
106 Godstone Road
Whyteleafe
CR3 0EB
Tel. 01-645 0469
Aims to help and support parents with problems through a

national network of 25 groups offering a telephone helpline service run by volunteer parents who have experienced stress. Callers may remain anonymous if they wish. Some groups offer further services as well, but the initial contact is always by telephone.

Homestart Consultancy
  140 New Walk
  Leicester LE1 7JL
  Tel. 0533 554988
Local Homestart schemes on a nationwide basis provide support, friendship and practical help to parents of under-5s.

Baby Stress

The National Childbirth Trust
  Alexandra House
  Oldham Terrace
  London W3 6NH
  Tel. 01-992 6762
The NCT is the foremost charity concerned with education for pregnancy, birth and parenthood, with over 300 branches and groups all over the country. Ante-natal classes, information, support and advice on breast-feeding, and post-natal support are the most important aspects of its work. Ante-natal classes usually consist of a course of eight sessions, during the last three months of pregnancy, directed by a group leader, who will also make fathers welcome in an informal and friendly atmosphere.

There are over 500 NCT breastfeeding counsellors throughout the country, and breast-feeding bras and pumps are among the many items offered on the NCT's maternity sales mail order catalogue. The NCT can also do much to help with the often daunting, as well as exciting, experience of coping with a new baby by putting new or expectant mothers in touch with members living nearby who offer friendship and the chance to meet socially and share experiences.

The NCT produces a series of leaflets and information sheets on many aspects of pregnancy, all revised periodically to keep them up to date, and holds a stock of recommended books, all of which can be ordered through the NCT's catalogue.

AIMS (Association for Improvements in the Maternity Services)
163 Liverpool Road
London N1 0RF
Tel. 01-278 5628
Offers information and advice on all aspects of maternity care, including parent's rights and choices available.

Maternity Alliance
15 Britannia Street
London WC1X 9JP
Tel. 01-837 1266
Member groups cover every aspect of pregnancy and mother-hood. The Alliance campaigns for better services for parents and babies and offers valuable advice on the financial benefits available to mothers.

SANDS (Stillbirth and Neonatal Death Society)
28 Portland Place
London W1N 3DE
Tel. 01-436 5881
A constantly expanding organization which aims to help all parents whose baby has died at or near birth. It provides various forms of stress-relief: a telephone support service from the central office, with alternative numbers on an answerphone outside office hours, and comfort from other bereaved parents, known as 'befrienders' who may also visit you in your own home if you wish. Local SANDS groups also offer the chance to meet collectively with other parents in the same situation: these are organized nationwide. All letters are answered personally and confidentially by the SANDS head office, and members receive a newsletter three times a year, designed to keep parents and groups in touch with each other, and containing shared experiences, group news, features and book reviews. SANDS also works closely with the many health professionals and other workers involved when a baby dies, and aims to help them increase their understanding of the stress the parents go through, by organizing and participating in lectures, conferences, workshops and study groups. Resource material published by SANDS includes a booklet for parents,

Saying Goodbye to Your Baby, which gives compassionate and practical advice, simply and sympathetically presented, on ways in which to come to terms with the event, as well as outlining the formalities that need to be completed. And their leaflet *Stillbirth and Neonatal Death: how you can help* suggests further ways in which friends, neighbours and other family members can help the bereaved parents come to terms with the stress of the situation.

Children Under Stress

National Association for the Welfare of Children in Hospital
Argyle House
29–31 Euston Road
London NW1 2SD
Tel. 01-833 2041

NAWCH works at national and local level, representing children's interests in the planning and delivery of health services, and advising and supporting parents of children admitted to hospital, conducting surveys, publishing reports and organizing conferences, seminars and study days. Its 10-point Charter is endorsed by many professional and voluntary bodies concerned with caring for sick children. NAWCH offers practical help with driving parents to hospital, providing play materials and running hospital play schemes, and encouraging the concept of parents and professionals working together, with the Room for Parents campaign. For parents, they publish a useful 32-page handbook, *Your Child in Hospital*, covering preparing for a hospital stay, talking to children about it, visiting, staying with your child in hospital, liaising with the medical team who will be caring for your child, and dealing with any problems on home-coming. There is also a leaflet, *Coming into Hospital*, and for children, an illustrated leaflet in comic strip form, *When I Went into Hospital*. Excellent reading lists are available with a wealth of publications suitable for children of up to 12 years concerning a variety of aspects of having medical tests and going into hospital.

Childline
Tel. 01-0800 1111

The free national helpline for children in trouble or danger, offering a 24-hour confidential counselling service.

Stress in Old Age

Pre-Retirement Association of Great Britain and Northern Ireland
19 Undine Street
London SW17 8PP
Tel. 01-767 3225

A registered charity, PRA is the major national member organization promoting education, planning, preparation and support activities for those requiring assistance in coping successfully with their retirement. PRA advises companies, public corporations and governmental bodies on pre-retirement education for older staff. It also specializes in seminars and study courses for individual members, who receive the monthly retirement magazine, *Choice*, and provides information on pre-retirement courses run by local education authorities, adult education institutes and voluntary educational bodies. There is a free PRA legal 'helpline' service, and free counselling over a range of financial questions.

Help the Aged
St James's Walk
London EC1R 0BE
Tel. 01-253 0253

Widely recognized as an authority on the needs of the elderly as well as for its international fund-raising activities. Help the Aged provides a valuable information service, backed up by a variety of leaflets on the special practical and emotional problems of old age, from footcare to taking precautions against doorstep salesmen, to bereavement. Help the Aged provides grants for organizations like Research into Ageing, to enable young people to find out more about elderly people's requirements, and to continue to work with them. Winter Warmthline and Be Safe are two of the major campaigns conducted by Help the Aged with government cooperation. Other practical ways in which the organization helps old people cope with special stresses include their community transport campaign and the community alarm programme, a 24-hour telephone-based link.

Age Concern (England)
60 Pitcairn Road
Mitcham
Surrey CR4 3LL
Tel. 01-640 5431

This other major organization for the care of the elderly also operates at three levels: fund raising; local groups offering a range of facilities; an information policy which includes dealing with problems and queries by telephone, and a letter-answering service.

National Carers' Association
29 Chilworth Mews
London W2 3RG
Tel. 01-724 7776

The Association aims to develop appropriate support for carers, that is, anyone whose life is in some way restricted because of the need to take responsibility for the care of a sick or elderly person. It encourages carers to recognize their own needs, and to cater for them through a national structure of 70 branches and groups. It provides information and advice, producing a number of fact sheets – for example, on finding your way round benefits.

The Association brings carers' needs and problems to the attention of government and other policy makers; its campaign Caring Costs, in collaboration with over 20 other voluntary organizations, aims to relieve financial hardship and stress for carers by helping them to achieve an adequate income.

Given that over a million people in Britain – husbands and wives, sons and daughters, parents and others – look after a relative who cannot manage alone at home, the scope of the Association's work is very wide-ranging, and through its carers' support groups does much to relieve the stress and strain of what can be emotionally and physically exhausting, isolating work.

State of Body

Alcohol Concern
305 Gray's Inn Road
London WC1X 8QF
Tel. 01-833 3471

Unlike Alcoholics Anonymous, Alcohol Concern, which is a national charity with central government funding, aims not at total abstinence, but safer drinking. Its main objectives are to raise public awareness of the risks of alcohol abuse, to inform and educate people about the recommended limits for drinking, to support and improve services for people with drink problems, and to promote action, locally and nationally, to prevent the harm caused by excessive drinking. Alcohol Concern encourages those who are experiencing stress through being close to someone with a drink problem, as well as drinkers themselves, to benefit from the help offered by alcohol information/counselling/advice services; contact can be made with local advice centres through Alcohol Concern, who supply listings.

Alcoholics Anonymous
  PO Box 1
  Stonebow House
  Stonebow
  York YO1 2NJ
  Tel. 0904 644026
A worldwide fellowship run on a voluntary basis – there are no membership fees – which aims to achieve total abstinence on a day to day basis by means of regular meetings offering group therapy and mutual support in terms of shared experiences. Members may attend as many meetings as they like and if they wish can be put in touch with other members via AA to make initial contact.

National Society of Non-Smokers
  Latimer House
  40–48 Hanson Street
  London W1P 7DE
  Tel. 01-636 9103
Through its Quit! campaign, probably best known to most people for National No Smoking Day, the Society offers information, with leaflets on such topics as the toxic substances in cigarette smoke, tips to family and friends on how best to help those who are giving up, and how to avoid putting on weight when you give up; a smoker's 'Quit Quickly' leaflet; telephone advice; courses

and counselling; project ideas for children; contact with Stop Smoking groups, and other organizations that can help, for example in the areas of hypnosis, acupuncture, and other forms of complementary medicine.

ASH (Action on Smoking and Health)
5–11 Mortimer Street
London W1N 7RH
Tel. 01-637 9843

A charity set up in 1971 by the Royal College of Physicians, to alert the public to the dangers of smoking, to prevent the death, disease and disability it causes, and to make non-smoking the norm in society. ASH is a public information campaign which gathers and disseminates up-to-date information on all kinds of issues by monitoring the local and national press, scientific and medical publications and trade magazines. ASH helps and encourages individuals who want to give up and promotes non-smoking policies in the workplace as well as campaigning for smoke-free space in public places. The ASH Awards Scheme honours individuals and organizations who have made an outstanding contribution to help reduce smoking.

National Back Pain Association
31–3 Park Road
Teddington
Middlesex TW11 0AB
Tel. 01 977 5474

Back pain is frequently related to stress, and the Association, which is a fund-raising organization for research into back problems, can put sufferers or anyone who is interested in contact with 50 self-help groups. These arrange monthly meetings with films and videos and talks by professionals, including osteopaths, aromatherapists and other practitioners of complementary medicine.

Migraine Trust
45 Great Ormond Street
London WC1N 3HD
Tel. 01-278 2676

Primarily a fund-raising organization for research purposes, the Trust also offers advice on self-help, and can send sufferers information from the Princess Margaret Migraine Clinic at Charing Cross Hospital.

Institute for Complementary Medicine
21 Portland Place
London W1N 3AF
Tel. 01-636 9543
Supplies information and sponsors research, education and training for developing new methods of natural health care.

International Federation of Aromatherapists
4 Eastmearn Road
London SE21 8HA

The British Medical Acupuncture Society
67–69 Chancery Lane
London WC2A 1AS
Holds a register of doctors who use acupuncture in their practice. List of names and addresses supplied.

The Council for Acupuncture
Suite 1
19a Cavendish Square
London W1M 9AD
Holds a register of non-medically qualified traditional acupuncturists.

Audio Ltd
26 Wendell Road
London W12 9RT
Tel. 01-743 1518/4352
Stocks a comprehensive range of biofeedback monitoring devices and accessories, some of which may also be hired. Brochures on individual instruments sent on request. Biofeedback books and cassettes are also available.

School of T'ai-Chi Ch'uan
  5 Tavistock Place
  London WC1
  Tel. 01-459 0764

This is a spiritual school teaching the T'ai-chi meditative art of movement and natural therapy in whole spiritual growth orientation. Study includes meditation for relaxation, centreing and expanding perception, breathing and body dynamics, healing, natural therapeutics, nature imagery, colour and sounds symbolism, philosophy related to modern life. Students are given personal guidance in limited size classes over a three-year full training course (four years for teachers). There are also shorter introductory courses, and workshops, lectures, and residential weekends. Private sessions may be arranged with the school's Director, for guidance in life direction, personal and relationship problems, massage, posture, stress and awareness relaxation therapy. Prospective students are welcome to watch classes and should telephone for an appointment.

Yoga for Health Foundation
  Ickwell Bury
  nr Biggleswade
  Beds
  Tel. 076 727 271

An organization which seeks to promote yoga in the belief that it is a vital approach to the many problems which beset us today.

The Foundation, which operates on a club basis in many parts of the world, trains yoga teachers, runs groups throughout the British Isles, and researches into the value of yoga in therapy. Its residential centre, located in a magnificent historic mansion set in beautiful grounds with a lake and nature reserve, offers a variety of facilities, activities and courses. Stays can be of any reasonable duration, and the daily yoga sessions can be tailormade to suit individual requirements, for novices and experienced yoga students alike. There is special emphasis on the value of yoga in coping with stress difficulties, and in opposing chronic disease, such as multiple sclerosis and other neurological diseases, arthritis, asthma, diabetes and cancer.

The Society of Teachers of the Alexander Technique
  10 London House
  266 Fulham Road
  London SW10 9EL
  Tel. 01-351 0828

State of Mind

Lifeskills
  3 Brighton Road
  London N2 8JU
  Tel. 01-346 9646

This company offers a practical series of tape cassette programmes and books designed to help handle a wide range of stressful situations in life. Each programme lasts 45–60 minutes. *Relax – and Enjoy It* is a complete course in deep, quick and differential relaxation, with techniques which provide the basis for anxiety management training, overcoming phobias, reduction of tension and fatigue, and good eating and sleep habits. In its sequel, *Control Your Tension*, the user is taught how to detect and use an anxiety surge as a trigger for quick relaxation and positive thinking strategy. Other cassettes available teach techniques for better sleep, self-assertion, handling interviews, studying effectively, passing exams, controlling fear of flying and agoraphobia.

Centre for Autogenic Training
  Positive Health Centre
  101 Harley Street
  London W1N 1DF
  Tel. 01-935 1811

The Centre runs autogenic training courses on a regular basis. Each course is limited to around eight people – an initial assessment by the Centre's specialist medical consultant is required before joining – and consists of eight sessions, once a week, lasting $1\frac{1}{2}$ hours each. Great emphasis is laid on the positive value of autogenics in controlling stress by means of passive concentration. The Centre also supplies a list of members of the British Association for Autogenic Training and Therapy, all of whom are willing to accept referrals for autogenic training.

Relaxation for Living
29 Burwood Park Road
Walton on Thames
Surrey KT12 5LH
Tel. 0932 227826

The aim of this registered charity is to promote the teaching of physical relaxation to combat the stress of modern life, to reduce fatigue, and to prevent ill health and promote healing by means of muscle relaxation. Day and evening classes – average number is eight in a class – are in courses of six or seven at weekly intervals, with a refresher 'booster' class after a few months. Pupils are of all ages. A correspondence course, with cassettes, is available. Practice and study tapes, and leaflets published by Relaxation for Living cover stress-related subjects such as heart disease, sounder sleep and better breathing, migraine, the menopause, easing grief, and posture, poise and confidence.

The Awakened Mind
9 Chatsworth Road
London NW2 4BJ (Isabel Maxwell Cade)

Courses and workshops on stress reduction, holistic health and relaxation, meditation, therapeutic massage, self-healing and new brain technology, with special emphasis on individual biofeedback. There are intensive one-day Saturday courses of five weekly sessions, with two seminars in each session. Isabel Maxwell Cade may also be contacted on certain days at Audio Ltd. (see page 125).

Westminster Pastoral Foundation
23 Kensington Square
London W8 5HN
01-937 6956

The Foundation's network of counselling centres all over the country offers a comprehensive range of counselling services including individual, group, marital and family counselling. Anyone can refer themselves and payment is according to means. The Foundation organizes a wide variety of training courses, full and part-time.